OF THE
SCOTTISH
CLANS

Helen Drever

Chambers

© This selection, estate of Helen Drever, 1989

Published by W & R Chambers Ltd Edinburgh, 1989
Reprinted 1989, 1990

British Library Cataloguing in Publication Data
Tales of the Scottish clans—[new ed].
  (Chambers mini guides)
  1. Scottish tales. Legends. Anthologies
  I. Title
  398.2'09411

  ISBN 0-550-20054-1

Cover design by John Marshall

Typeset by Bookworm Typesetting Ltd, Edinburgh
Printed in Singapore by
Singapore National Printers Ltd

Contents

Foreword

MOST of these Clan Tales were originally written for the BBC, and were broadcast during Scottish Children's Hour. Borrowed, as they are, from a variety of sources, it is almost inevitable that there should be slight historical inaccuracies in the tales. But even historians differ in their accounts of happenings among the Scottish clans, so I may claim indulgence for a mere story-teller!

It is impossible to name all the sources of the tales. In addition to books on individual clans, the historians – Browne, Stewart, Gordon and Hume Brown – supplied a good deal of material; so did Eyre-Todd's *Clan History*, Mackay's *Clan Warfare*, and Johnston's *Scottish Clans*. And many of the stories and legends I heard from old folks in the Highlands, who had heard them from their parents and grandparents.

H.D.

Introduction

The Loch of the Swords

A Clan Dispute

I WONDER whether you have ever heard how the Scottish Clans came into being. It was in this way. The people who lived in the Highlands of Scotland in far-off days had to find some means of protecting themselves and their families from invasion and from being attacked by strong and fierce and often greedy neighbours.

In those days there was no quick way of getting about the country. There were no railways and no motor cars; even the roads were very few and *very* bad!

And although there was always a King of Scotland who made laws, and who appointed officers to carry out these laws and to keep order, there was little or no chance of getting the help of these officials in any dispute because of the great distance and the difficulty of travel. The country was divided into valleys – or straths as they are called – in which the Highlanders lived.

These straths were separated by mountains, rivers and lochs, and by great stretches of moor. Because of this the people were divided into little communities, or Clans, as they were called. A Clan was made up of people, all bearing the same surname and believing themselves to be related to one another and to be descended from the same ancestors. The head of the family was called the Chief of the Clan, and his castle was a kind of palace, to which every man of the Clan was welcome, and to which they all rallied when war broke out.

There were a great many Clans. It was said that at the Battle of Bannockburn at least eighteen Highland chieftains brought their clansmen into the field to support Robert the Bruce. That was in the year 1314. And, just six hundred years later, when the Great War began, the same clan-names were to be found among the soldiers of the Highland regiments; and among the officers in 1914 there were many direct descendants of the Clan chiefs who fought at Bannockburn!

Each Clan had its own war-cry – or 'slogan' – to which every clansman was bound to respond. The slogan was a watch-word in cases of sudden alarm, in the confusion of battle, or in the darkness of night. And every Clan had a place at which they met when the Chief needed help.

In any emergency notice was given to the Clan and those in alliance with them by sending out the Fiery Cross or Tarie. This signal consisted of two pieces of wood in the form of a cross. One of the ends of the horizontal piece was set alight, and from the other end was hung a piece of linen or white cloth stained with blood.

Two fast runners of the Clan, each with a Fiery Cross in his hand, were sent out by the Chief in opposite directions, and, as they ran, they shouted the war-cry of the tribe, and the name of the place where the clansmen were to meet.

When a man became tired he handed over the Cross to another of the Clan, who went on with it. So, as each bearer went at full speed, the Clan was assembled in wonderfully short time.

Land and cattle were the principal possessions of a Clan, and of course well-watered land which was good for grazing cattle was very valuable indeed.

Cattle-stealing (or 'lifting', as it was called) was very common, and Clans were continually at war with each other on this account, or about the boundaries of their land.

Sometimes these boundary disputes were settled by agreement between the heads of the Clans, and the following is the story of one of these settlements.

The scene of the story was a small loch called 'Loch-na-Clive', which means 'The Loch of the Swords', in the centre of which three counties meet – Inverness-shire, Perthshire and Argyllshire.

The story relates that two powerful Clans, Cameron of Lochiel and Murray of Atholl, had, for many years, been at enmity over certain land boundaries. The Chief of the Cameron Clan – and the Earl of Atholl – Chief of the Murrays – arranged to meet by the side of Loch-na-Clive, in order to settle the dispute. And the chiefs were to come without any followers and just talk the matter over. It was a fine day in late summer. The hills were blue, the water of the rivers and lochs sparkled in the sunshine, and the heather glowed gorgeously purple as Lochiel, accompanied by his favourite collie-dog, walked along to the trysting-place by Loch-na-Clive.

On the way from his own country of Lochaber, Lochiel was met by an old woman of the Clan Cameron, who stopped him on the moor and asked anxiously, 'Where are your men, Lochiel?'

Lochiel just laughed, and said that he needed no men to-day.

But the old woman kept her eyes fixed steadily on his face, and croaked again, 'Where are your men, Lochiel?'

'Peace, old witch!' said Lochiel, 'what need have I to-day of a following? I go only to meet Atholl, my brother Chief,' and strode on.

But the uncanny old woman hobbled after him, caught the flowing end of his cloak and uttered again, 'Where are your men, Lochiel?'

The Chief could not help feeling uneasy at this obstinate suggestion of danger and he returned to the nearest clachan (or village) and collected a following of sixty-five men.

THE LOCH OF THE SWORDS

They followed him stealthily and when he reached
Loch-na-Clive they hid in the deep heather above the
loch. Presently the Earl of Atholl was seen striding
through the heather, alone, and Lochiel felt ashamed
of his hidden company. The two chiefs greeted each
other and began to talk of the business about which
they had met. But they could not agree, and soon they
came to high words. Suddenly Atholl waved his hand
in the air and twenty Atholl Highlanders sprang up
from the heather behind him.

'Who are these?' said Lochiel.

'Atholl wethers,' said the Earl, with meaning in his
tone. 'They have come to graze on Lochaber
pastures.'

Lochiel had arranged with his men that if he needed
their help he would turn his cloak so as to show the red
lining. So there was a wave of bright red where he
stood, and instantly his three-score-and-five warriors
came bounding down to the loch side.

Atholl started; and, 'Who are these?' said he.

'Lochaber dogs,' said Lochiel, 'sharp-toothed and
hungry, and keen to taste the flesh of your Atholl
wethers! Give up, my Lord Earl, your claim to the
land, for my dogs are fierce and I cannot much longer
hold them in leash!'

The two chiefs looked at each other, and presently
Atholl smiled and held out a hand, which Lochiel
grasped.

At that sign of peace, both 'dogs' and 'wethers'
retreated, and sank down again among the heather;
and the chiefs, now in friendly spirit, discussed the
business of the boundary.

A settlement was at length reached, and the Earl of
Atholl, drawing his sword from its sheath and kissing
it, renounced his claim to the land in dispute 'through
summer's heat and winter's cold.' Then he whirled it
round his head and with a great sweep it disappeared
in the waters of Loch-na-Clive. And Atholl proclaimed
that until the sword was found again, the land should
be Lochiel's land.

Three centuries have passed since then; but one day
about a hundred years ago a boy fishing in the loch
drew up a rusty broadsword with a basket hilt, and,
very much pleased with his strange 'fish', carried it up

to show the minister of the parish. But the Lochaber men were much alarmed at hearing of the boy's unusual 'catch' and they would not sleep a night until it was restored to the watery bed where it had slept for two hundred years!

1

Somerled of the Isles

Ancestor of Clan Donald

SUCH reliable information as we possess about the forebears of Clan Donald starts with Gille Adamnan, the grandfather of Somerled of the Isles. For many years before Somerled's time the north and west of Scotland was being harassed by the raids of powerful enemies from outside the kingdom. These were the Northmen – or Vikings – who came from Norway, Sweden and Denmark. They were splendid fighters and born sailors, their ships being the largest and fastest on the seas. These ships were shaped like dragons, the bow being built to look like a dragon's head, while the stern formed its tail. There were places for as many as sixty rowers in most of the viking ships. At first these Norsemen landed only to plunder and destroy, and dash off again. But a time came when they were not content to stop at that – when their ideas was to conquer land in which to settle.

The islands were fairly easy prey for them, and in course of time they took possession of Orkney, Shetland, and the Western Isles; and parts of Caithness

and Sutherland as well. Then they turned their
attention to the mainland of Argyll. Somerled's
grandfather owned a large part of Argyll, but he was
not powerful enough to keep the vikings at bay, and
after one ineffectual attempt he was driven out of the
country. With his son, Gillebrighde or Gilbert, he took
refuge in the north of Ireland, where he died. By and
by Gilbert began to long to see his native land again,
and he and his son, named Somerled, managed to
return to Argyll. But they found themselves homeless
wanderers there, and they settled in a cave on the
shores of Loch Linnhe, where they lived in direst
poverty.

Gilbert's fighting days were over, and Somerled
spent his time in brooding over the ruined fortunes of
his house. But something happened to change all this,
and, from being a depressed dreamer, Somerled
suddenly developed into a master of warlike
strategy.

The Clan MacInnes (who are a sept or ally of the
Clan Macdonald) had come to Morven in Argyll on a
foraging expedition. The Norsemen appeared
unexpectedly, and in a skirmish with them the
MacInnes leader was killed. So the Clan found
themselves leaderless, and practically in sight of the
enemy as well, for the viking galleys lay just off the
shore. No man among the clansmen was qualified to
lead them into battle, and they knew of no one on the
spot who could step into the breach. So they formed a
council which agreed on rather a reckless plan. This
was to go along the shore hills and invite the first
person whom they should see to become their leader
against the vikings! They set off and, when they had
reached the rocky banks of a fishing stream called the
'Gearr Abhainn' ('Garven'), whom should they see
but Somerled with his rod, angling for his next meal!

In spite of their desperate situation they could not
help raising a great shout of laughter! Somerled asked
the reason for their mirth. It was rather an awkward
question to answer, but they said it was just a shout of
joy at seeing him! The fact was that they looked upon
poor Somerled as a sort of half-wit because of his
melancholy manner. But they had sworn to take as
leader the first man they should see, and in fulfilment

2

of that vow they now asked Somerled to be their leader. He thought about it for some time without answering, and suddenly there came a tug at his line! 'See now,' he said, 'I have hooked a salmon. Let it give you my answer. If I can land the fish, my help shall be yours!' As it happened, it was a very sportive fish and difficult to catch, and the MacInnes men saw a thrilling fight between man and salmon as it plunged and struggled up and down the river. But Somerled was a good fisher, and at last the salmon lay quivering on the bank. Then Somerled turned and said, 'My help is yours! But – to begin with – having of your own accord invited me to lead you, you must swear to obey my commands.' Quite delighted at this exhibition of authority from the supposed dreamer, they acknowledged their new general and gave him on the spot their oath of allegiance.

He appointed a place where they were to muster, and giving orders to light a great number of fires round their encampment, he said that he would join them later. He carried the salmon to the cave, where he cooked it and left it ready for his father's meal; and then went to take up his command.

At early morning he saw the viking ships landing their forces. These completely outnumbered his men; so he made a plan by which to deceive the enemy as to his own numbers. A herd of cattle lay in a neighbouring valley and he at once ordered them to be killed and skinned. He occupied a position which commanded a full view of the enemy's movements; and as soon as he saw them forming their ranks he ordered his small force to march down the valley and go round a hill at the foot – coming back to the place where they started from. They kept on marching round and round the hill, and the enemy thought that they were a formidable battalion. Next, ordering every man to wrap himself in an ox hide with the smooth side out, they did the same thing all over again several times, which gave the appearance of another (and different) battalion. After that Somerled ordered his men to turn the *rough* side of the hides outward, and the wild and savage appearance of this supposed *third* battalion was too much for the Norsemen, who, falling into disorder, gave way to panic and fled in all directions. Seeing this, Somerled and his fierce-looking little force, wildly yelling, charged down the slope, and cut down the viking advance party with great slaughter. The rest made for the ships and got away as fast as possible.

Somerled followed up his victory with others, and eventually driving the Norsemen out of the Western Highlands, he made himself master of Lochaber, Morven, and northern Argyll. Meanwhile, David II was driving them from the Isle of Man, Arran and Bute, and Somerled for his assistance and daring got a grant of these islands from the King.

In the Western Isles, however, the viking power was still unbroken, and he was determined to be ruler of these also. The King of the Isles at that time was a viking called Olaf the Red, who had a daughter, Ragnhildis. Somerled made up his mind that, although he could not take the islands by force, there was a way of getting a footing there. This was to marry Ragnhildis. Whether Ragnhildis wanted to marry Somerled did not enter into the question, but he carried her off.

Perhaps she did not mind being carried off by such a famous warrior; she certainly married him! They had three sons, Dugall, Reginald and Angus. Dugall founded the Clan MacDougal, and inherited Lorn, Jura and Mull when his father died. Reginald got Kintyre and Islay; and Bute and Arran fell to Angus.

Reginald, through his son Donald, founded the famous Clan MacDonald. He took the title of 'King', and later 'Lord of the Isles', which latter became a hereditary title in the family.

Clan MacDonald, which was very powerful and included many branches, always took a prominent share in the turmoils which kept the Highlands in active ferment during several hundred years. They were entirely loyal to the Stewarts, and took an active share in helping and sheltering Prince Charlie in his wanderings after Culloden.

2

Clan Campbell

The Legend of Kilchurn

THE pedigree of the Campbells can be traced back to the thirteenth century when the family was first mentioned in important Scottish documents. They got that name, it is said, because of an ancestor who had a facial peculiarity of some sort, for in the Gaelic the words 'cam beul' mean 'wry mouth'.

Highland names were often the result of some personal defect or attribute, 'Malcolm Canmore', for instance. 'Can mohr' means the 'big head', and so we got 'Malcolm with the Big Head'.

Campbell is the surname of the Dukes of Argyll. The first Duke was called 'Cailean Mor', which means 'Big Colin'; and ever since his day the Clan title for the Chief has been 'Mic Cailean Mor', or 'Son of Big Colin'. The Dukes of Argyll are looked up to with the most profound reverence by their kinsmen and clansmen, and are regarded by them as more important than Royalty itself! When Queen Victoria's daughter, the Princess Louise, married the Marquis of Lorne (who was the eldest son of the Duke of Argyll) the Campbell Clan did not consider that a special honour had been paid to the Scottish family! Not a bit of it! 'Isn't it proud that the Queen will be this day, that her daughter has got the son of Mic Cailean Mor for her husband!'

Next in rank to the Dukes of Argyll are their cousins, the Campbells of Breadalbane. The ancestor of this branch was Sir Colin Campbell — 'Cailean Dubh na Roimhe' (Black Colin of Rome). He received, as his inheritance from his father, the lands of Glenorchy, after the MacGregors had been driven from them. And here is a story of that Sir Colin, Knight-Templar and Lord of Kilchurn Castle — the ruins of which can still be seen on a peninsula on Loch Awe in Argyllshire.

Judging from what remains of the castle and from the commanding position which it occupies, it is easy to see that it must have been in its day a very important stronghold. There was a great tower, five stories high, which is said to have been planned and added to by Lady Campbell, when her husband was away fighting in the Crusades. The Knights Templars were the most important and most powerful of the great military orders of the Middle Ages. The object of the order was a noble one. It was to maintain, by force of arms if necessary, a free passage for pilgrims who wanted to visit the Holy Sepulchre in Jerusalem. Fighting in the Crusades meant long absence from home, so, when Sir Colin went away to Europe and Palestine, his lady knew that there would be a period of loneliness before her, with but scanty news of her husband's doings.

Accompanying Sir Colin on the expedition were men of his own Clan, one of whom was sent back to Scotland at regular intervals to tell Lady Campbell and their young son how Sir Colin was getting on. During his absence which had extended over seven years, he was for a time in Rome, where he had a very singular and disturbing dream about his wife and his home. He tried to forget the dream, but it preyed on his mind to such an extent that he confided it to one of the monks. In those days people believed greatly in dreams and what they foretold, and the monk at once advised Sir Colin to go home, because, in his opinion, a very serious domestic calamity threatened. Acting on his advice Sir Colin left for Scotland. After encountering many dangers and difficulties he reached a place near Glasgow called Succoth, which is still owned by a branch of the Campbell family. At Succoth there lived an old woman of his Clan. This old woman in his early days had been his nurse. In the disguise of a beggar he arrived at her cottage at nightfall and knocked at the door. When she opened the door she saw what she supposed to be a poor beggar man, who asked her for food and shelter. She at once asked him to come in and sit by the fire, and she set about making some porridge for her visitor. As he stretched out his hands to the blaze of the fire, her startled eyes lighted on a peculiarly shaped scar on his arm. 'Oh, Cailean Dubh, Cailean Dubh! my bairn that I nursed!' she cried. 'It is myself that knows that scar!' and she wept in her joy, for she had supposed him to be dead. She hastened to tell him all that had happened in his absence, and the story supplied a reason for the uneasiness caused by his dream. It appeared that for some years no word of any kind had been received in Argyllshire with regard to Sir Colin, nor had any of the letters been delivered which he had sent to his wife. Not only that, but news had been circulated that he had been killed in battle in the Holy Land.

Now Sir Colin knew that someone must have played him false; he had repeatedly sent home clansmen with letters and news for his wife, and it was scarcely possible that *every* messenger sent by him should have perished before reaching Scotland. His old nurse was able to supply the explanation and justify his suspicions.

All the rumours about his death had come apparently from one source. This was a neighbouring laird, the Baron McCorquodale, who – as was eventually proved – had intercepted and killed or else imprisoned every one of Sir Colin's messengers. By degrees he induced Lady Campbell to believe in her husband's death, and at last he proposed marriage to her; and she (believing that he was her best friend) accepted him.

This was the news that his old nurse had for Sir Colin; and further, the marriage was fixed for the following day! Indignant at what he had heard, Sir Colin set out for Kilchurn early next morning. As he followed the romantic windings of the River Orchy, the lively sounds of the bagpipe and the gay shouts of his clansmen assembled to join in the festivity were borne to his ears on the breeze. He crossed the drawbridge and entered the gates of the castle, which on this important occasion were open to all. Nobody recognised him, for he still wore his beggar's rags. He stood for a little, silently gazing on the scene of excitement and feasting, until one of the servants asked him what he wanted. 'To have my hunger satisfied and my thirst quenched,' he said; and at once food and drink were brought to him. He ate, but he refused to drink, making the request that the lady of the castle would give him a cup with her own hands and allow him to drink to her health. Lady Campbell was told of this strange request from a beggar; and being always charitable and benevolent he came at once and handed him a cup of wine. Sir Colin drank to her health, and as he handed back the empty cup he dropped a ring into it. The lady observing his action took out the ring and examined it. To her amazement she found it to be a ring which she had given to her husband when he departed for the Holy Land, and which he had promised to keep as a talisman on the field of battle and his most sacred possession. Greatly agitated she said to the beggar, 'Speak, man! Where got ye this ring? Got ye it on sea or got ye it on land, or got ye it on a dead man's hand?' And Sir Colin, gazing earnestly at her, said, 'I neither got it on sea, nor got it on land, nor yet on a dead man's hand. I got it from you on our parting day and I give it to you on your wedding day!' With that he let his beggar's cloak fall from him and he stood revealed to the astonished company in the white cloak of the Knight-Templar with the scarlet cross on the breast – their own lost Sir Colin!

'Oh! my husband, my husband!' cried Lady Campbell, full of joy, as she threw herself into his arms. A shout of delight from his clansmen rent the air, and the pipers made the castle resound with the pibroch of the Campbells. Baron McCorquodale was allowed to depart unnoticed. In their joy at being reunited, Sir Colin and his lady were generous to the traitor and let him go unpunished.

But after the death of Sir Colin some years later, his son, 'Black Colin' the second, avenged the wrong done to his father, and took from the Baron his lands and possessions.

3

Clan Mackenzie

The Caberfeidh

HUNDREDS of years ago, a song made in praise of the Chief of the Clan Mackenzie began like this:

'Kenneth MacKenneth, great Earl of the North, The Lord of Loch Carron, Glenshiel and Seaforth.'

Now, looking at a map of Ross-shire you see that Glencarron and Glenshiel are on the west of the county, while on the east, not very far from Dingwall, is Brahan Castle and Seaforth's largest estate. So that the old saying, that 'the lands of the Mackenzies stretched from sea to sea' was quite true. Two earldoms (those of Seaforth and Cromartie) belong to the Clan, as well as four baronetcies. The Mackenzies have always been a loyal Clan. One chief went with James I on an expedition to the north; another fought with James IV at Flodden, and was nearly captured by the English. A third fought for Mary Queen of Scots at the Battle of Langside.

The Clan took part in several Jacobite risings and had their estates forfeited to the Crown. They were also deprived of the Earldom of Seaforth. But the Kenneth who was the Chief in 1770 bought back his property from the Crown and was again made Earl of Seaforth. To show his gratitude he and the Clan the following year raised the regiment of the Seaforth Highlanders.

The crest used by the Chief of the Clan is a stag's head and the granting of this crest makes an interesting story.

Back in the thirteenth century, Alexander III, King of Scotland, was hunting in the Forest of Mar in the Grampian Mountains. A royal stag hunt – to which the chiefs of all the great Highland Clans had been invited – was in progress. Among the chief was Kenneth of Kintail, Chief of the Mackenzies. It was a fine day for sport. The hounds were keen on the scent, and stag after stag fell to the arrows of the party – for in those days firearms were not used for sport. The King, who was a very enthusiastic sportsman. spied away up the valley the great antlers of a fine stag, and the hounds were sent to drive it down. This they did, and down the gully towards the King and his companions came the handsome hunted beast. To the dismay of Alexander and the horror of his company, the infuriated animal lowered its antlers and charged straight at the King, who was entirely at its mercy. Before any of the other chieftains could stir, Kenneth of Kintail dashed to the King's rescue, shouting the Gaelic words, 'Cuidich an Righ! Cuidich an Righ!' ('Save the King! Save the King!') He drew his bow; an arrow sped through the air. It was a risky shot, for it might easily have hit the King instead of the stag. But Kenneth aimed true. The arrow pierced the stag – and the King was saved! The King in token of his gratitude granted to the Mackenzie Chief a stag's head, to be the armorial bearings of the family for all time, with the motto 'Cuidich an Righ', and confirmed him in possession of the lands of Kintail.

Five hundred years later, when the regiment of the Seaforth Highlanders was raised, they were allowed to use both crest and motto. It is the only Highland regiment in the Army which uses a Clan crest and motto.

The Macdonalds of the Isles (Somerled's descendants) were at one time the most powerful Clan in the Highlands. When they went to war they could demand, as a right, the military help of the Mackenzies and the Rosses. But when these Clans themselves grew powerful, they broke away from the Lord of the Isles and refused to take part in his quarrels. Feeling ran high then, especially between the Mackenzies and the Macdonalds, until the fifteenth century, when Kenneth, the son of the Chief of Kintail, married a daughter of the Lord of the Isles. But no peace could last between these Clans and very soon there was a new quarrel. One of those Macdonalds who had come into possession of Balconie Castle, on the Cromarty Firth, gave a great entertainment to the gentry of Ross-shire, who poured in from all over the county. Night quarters were allotted to the guests as they arrived, for hospitality in the Highlands was no one-night affair; it was on a most lavish scale and lasted for several days. Almost the last to come, as it happened (and rather an unexpected guest) was Kenneth of Kintail, with a band of his clansmen. Macdonald had by this time allotted all the sleeping-rooms in the castle – what on earth was to be done with the Mackenzies? The only place available was a large kiln and this he offered to Kenneth and his party, with the hint that as he was now a relative by marriage, he would not expect to stand on ceremony. But the offer was taken as a deliberate insult; Kenneth flew into a great rage and out came the Mackenzies' weapons! But Kenneth restrained them and retired with them to the Black Isle, to settle how to avenge the affront. The news went round the rest of the Clan, which rose in its wrath and made ready for battle. But first of all Kenneth was determined in his rage to be done with the Macdonalds for good – and he sent his wife back to her family. It is said that she was blind in one eye and that he added insult to injury by sending, as her escort, a one-eyed servant, a one-eyed horse, and a one-eyed dog! Naturally that added fuel to the Macdonald fire. The Battle of the Park – as it was called – between the two Clans took place at Jamestown, between Strathpeffer and the River Conon. The men of Strathconon (who were mostly

MacLennans and MacRaes, septs of the Caberfeidh) were the most famous archers in the Highlands, so you may be sure they were called on to rally to Kenneth's standard. In the battle Kenneth scored a great victory and, in defeating the Macdonalds, he struck a blow which had lasting effects on Highland history. His name has been handed down to his descendants as 'Kenneth of the Battle'.

At that time the River Conon, being in flood, was very wide, and the routed Macdonalds could not find the fords by which to cross. It is said that, after the battle, an old Jamestown woman who was cutting fodder for her cow was asked by some retreating Macdonalds 'where the ford was?' She said, 'Iss it the ford you are wanting? Well, indeed, and iss not the whole river just a big ford!' Believing her, they dashed into the river, which at once swept them off their feet. One or two of them grasped tree-branches overhanging the banks, whereupon this bloodthirsty old dame promptly used a sickle and cut the branches to which the men clung! As they were swept away she said, 'Thieves that you are, be going! The Mackenzies will not grudge you a few of their branches!'

After the Battle of Culloden, the quick wit and devotion of a member of the Mackenzie Clan greatly helped Prince Charlie when he was hard pressed. This was Roderick Mackenzie, who had served as one of the Prince's life-guards. About the same age and build, his features were sufficiently like those of Charles to deceive a casual observer. Near the Prince's hiding-place in Glenmoriston he was surprised and overcome by some of Cumberland's soldiers, who were all eager to win the £30000 which had been set on the Prince's head. Nothing could save Roderick, but he saw a way to shield Charles, and he called out loudly as he fell, 'Villains! you have killed your Prince! You have killed your Prince!' The soldiers who had not been quite certain of the identity of their victim were overjoyed at their supposed good fortune, and hurried to claim the £30000. The Duke of Cumberland, equally delighted, immediately set off for London to have the head identified as that of Princes Charles. The mistake was of course discovered, but the delay enabled the Prince to escape from Glenmoriston and take refuge with Cluny Macpherson at 'The Cage'. And now, away above Glenmoriston can be seen a great heap of stones which is called 'Mackenzie's Cairn'. It is a lasting memorial to the resource and sacrifice of Roderick of the Caberfeidh.

Shortly after the Seaforth Highlanders had been raised in Ross-shire, the regiment marched to Leith to embark for foreign service. While at Leith some cause of discontent occurred among them and they refused to disembark. Instead, they marched out of the town with pipes playing and two Mackenzie tartan plaids for regimental colours fixed on poles. They marched up Arthur's Seat and stayed there for several days, getting supplies from people who sympathised with them. The Earls of Seaforth and Dunmore and other Highland gentlemen made inquiries into the causes of their complaints and, finding these justified, had them removed; so the soldiers, being now satisfied, marched down the hill with the pipes playing and the two earls and General Skene at their head. The Highlanders went back to Leith, pleased that they had proved their Highland independence. It was said that the MacRaes, who were strongly represented in the regiment, were the ringleaders in this disturbance, which has always been known as 'The Affair of the MacRaes'.

4

Clan Mackay of Strathnaver

Siol Mhorgan

FEW of the Highland Clans are so uncertain of their
origin as the Mackays of Strathnaver – or Clan Morgan
as they were first called. The popular opinion is that
they were derived from the same root as the Forbeses,
who are an Aberdeenshire Clan. This opinion is
supported by an eleventh-century manuscript which
shows that the lands of the Abbey of Deer, in
Aberdeenshire, were granted to Clan Morgan. The
Mackays themselves must have believed in the Forbes
connection because, in 1608, they adopted the
Forbes badge and armorial bearings (with slight
differences) by permission of Lord Forbes, whom
Mackay of Farr called his 'Dear Chief'.

Norwegian sagas tell us that the ancestor of the race
was a 'Jarl' – which probably means the same thing as
a 'Mormaer', the old Celtic title of the ruler of a
province.

It is practically certain that the original Clan Mackay
or Morgan was one of the warlike tribes that Malcolm
IV could not control in Moray, as Aberdeenshire was

15

called, when Angus, and later his son MacEth, were rulers of the province. At last Malcolm split up the tribes, expelling them by force to various parts of the country.

The Clan Morgan went northwards, where MacEth's daughter was married to the Norse Earl of Caithness; and he gave the incomers the Strath of Naver in which to settle. There they were surrounded by powerful Clans.

South of them were the Macleods and the Earl of Sutherland; east of them the Gunns and the Sinclairs.

They had no charter of land from the King; they held their land entirely by the sword until the year 1499.

For about a hundred and fifty years they warred, now with one neighbour, now with another; occasionally combining with one of the very tribes against whom their attacks had previously been directed.

According to the historian, Sir Robert Gordon, the Chief of their tribe left two sons, called Morgan and Farquhar. Through Morgan came the Clan name 'Siol Mhorgan' (the race of Morgan). A son married a MacNeil of Gigha and the son of his marriage was a born leader. He was named 'Aodh' (Lye), and from him the Clan took its name MacAodh or Mackay.

Angus Dubh (Black Angus) was another famous Mackay warrior. He was known as 'Angus the Absolute' and it was said that he could summon four thousand men to the field.

When James I came to Scotland, one of his first acts was, under pretence of friendship, to invite forty of the great Highland chiefs to meet him in Inverness. But when the chiefs appeared they were all made prisoners by the King. Angus was among them and before he could be set free he had to give his son Neil as a hostage. Poor Neil was kept prisoner on the Bass Rock for ten years, and meanwhile Angus sent for 'Iain Aberach', his youngest son, who had been brought up in Lochaber among his mother's people. Iain obeyed his father's summons at once, walking all the long way from Lochaber to Strathnaver, through the wild mountains of Inverness-shire, by the wide firths and fertile lands of Easter Ross, and on through the broad moors and great bens of Sutherland. He carried no baggage. His plaid served him as cloak by day and blanket by night. When he arrived he was tired and hungry, and he asked for food. Angus told him that he would find all he wanted 'and perhaps more' in the dining-chamber – so off Iain went. He opened the door and saw food in abundance on the able, but the food was guarded by a great fierce boar-hound! That was Angus's way of testing the courage of his young (and almost unknown) son! The animal bounded towards the stranger and leapt at his throat – truly a strange welcome for a hungry lad! But Iain was brave though hungry and he had just time to snatch out his dirk when the hound was upon him. He struck with sure aim – and yet unwillingly, for he hated killing such a beautiful dog. But Angus was glad to see that the men of Lochaber had taught his boy to carry a stout heart, and in his joy he exclaimed, 'Dearbh thu do chridhe!' ('You have proved your valour!') And ever since the Aberach family have used these words as their motto or war-cry, 'Bi treun!' ('Be valiant!') being the slogan of all the other Mackays.

Before he died, Angus the Absolute was to see this young son of his 'prove his valour' in a great battle in which he led the Mackays to victory. This was at Drumnacoub near Tongue, against the Earl of Sutherland. By that time Angus was past wielding a sword in battle; but he met his death on the field all the same. After the fight was over he went to see what he could do for his wounded clansmen, and he was killed by an arrow from a skulking assassin of a Sutherland man! Naturally that made the feud more bitter than ever and clan fights succeeded each other year in and year out.

There was one occasion when the Mackays got into dreadful disgrace. A party led by Neil's son chased some enemies into the Chapel of St Duthus at Tain, in Ross-shire, and killed them. Not content with that they set fire to the chapel! The Tain people were of course furious, for the church was considered to be sanctuary for refugees. Besides which, was it not in that very chapel that Malcolm Canmore had granted a Royal Charter to the Burgh of Tain! It was a terrible deed and the Mackay leader was captured and executed.

In the time of Charles I, Donald, Chief of the Clan, was raised to the peerage and became Lord Reay. One result of these centuries of clan feuds had been to make a splendid fighting race of the Mackays. Lord Reay saw this and he organised their fighting powers by raising a brigade of over two thousand men for military service with the King of Denmark. After this service, they enlisted under Prince Gustavus Adolphus of Sweden, and fought for the Protestant cause in Europe in the Thirty Years' War. During that war the Mackays distinguished themselves over and over again, and earned the greatest praise for their endurance and valour. They in turn regarded the Prince with great respect and affection. They paid him what is considered a high honour in the Highlands, when his name was given to many a Mackay baby born about that time, and since handed down in their families. So if we meet someone called Gustavus Mackay, we may safely conclude that one of his ancestors fought under the Swedish Prince three hundred years ago.

An officer of the Mackay Brigade, General Hugh Mackay of Scourie, was so distinguished as to be invited by two kings at the same time to come and command their rival armies! These kings were William of Orange and James II of England. The general accepted William's offer and went to Holland; and so began the Dutch connection of the Mackays. One branch of the family settled there and was granted a title and an estate by the Government of Holland.

Another member of the Clan was a distinguished poet called Rob Donn Mackay, whose poems are among the best in Gaelic literature. He began life as a herdsman and afterwards became the steward of Lord Reay. When he was forty-five years of age a French invasion threatened our shores and the Earl of Sutherland raised a battalion of Sutherland Highlanders to help defend them. Some people say that poets are dreamers, but Rob Donn was no dreamer, for he at once offered himself and served in the regiment for eight years. Not a bit like a certain bard belonging to another Clan, who began fighting in a battle, but, when things got very hot, he ran away and hid himself. He explained afterwards that, of course, he wasn't a bit *afraid* – or anything of that sort – but that it would be such a pity if no one could write a poem about the battle, and he was just making sure!

After that war Lord Reay sold Strathnaver to the Earl of Sutherland, so that there is very little Mackay land now in the North of Scotland.

It is a long, long time since these feuds, and the Mackays live now at peace with their neighbours. But for years jealousy smouldered amongst the dependants of the rival chiefs, and offence was always quick to be taken. There is a story that once the Earl of Sutherland sent one of his retainers with a message from Dunrobin Castle to the House of Tongue, Lord Reay's family seat. It is a long distance away and the Dunrobin man had to stay at Tongue overnight. At bedtime he took off his shoes (or 'cuarans', as they were called) of undressed leather, and put them on the dresser in the kitchen; which annoyed the cook exceedingly, for she took it as a deliberate insult. Next morning, for breakfast, she gave the Dunrobin man a very large substantial-looking pie. He ate every bit of it, and then he said he must be 'taking the road', and would she get his cuarans for him? She gave a peculiar smile and said to him, 'Well now, I hope that you enjoyed your breakfast?' 'Yes, inteet,' he answered. 'It was the fine breakfast whatefer. Inteet, I'm thinking I'll not be needing any dinner after it, at all, at all! But now I am looking for my cuarans, for I must be going.' 'Well indeed,' said the cook, 'it's not looking for your cuarans you need to be, for they are inside you – and a fine breakfast they made whatefer! And that will be teaching you to put your upstart Sutherland cuarans on a shentleman's dresser!'

5

Clan Cameron

The Cameron Men

THE name 'Cameron' is made up of two Gaelic words – 'cam', meaning wry or crooked, and 'sron' meaning nose. So an ancestor of the Clan must have had a crooked nose! The first Cameron chief who was famous in history was Donald Dhu (Black Donald), and each chief since his time has been called Mic Donuil Dhu (Son of Black Donald). The Camerons have a belief that they are descended from one of the Danish royal family, who, fifteen years ago, helped a Scottish king to win back his throne. But whatever their origin, whether royal or merely noble, it is certain that no name is more popular in the Highlands than that of Cameron. And the name of Lochiel, the Chief of the Clan, has always stood for everything that is honourable and good.

Lochaber in Inverness-shire is the home country of the clan. It is a wild and beautiful region, broken up by great bens and glens, with lovely lochs and rushing mountain rivers to keep it green and fertile.

The way in which places and family names are allied is characteristic all through the Highlands. Who, for example, can separate the name of Glencoe from thoughts of the Macdonalds; Appin from the Stewarts; Balquhidder from the Maclarens and Macgregors? – and so on.

So it is in Lochaber. The mere mention of Loch Eil, Loch Arkaig, Loch Lochy – and the Camerons are with us! – Sir Ewan, who was such a thorn in the side of Cromwell's soldiers; the Gentle Lochiel of Prince Charlie's day; Dr Archie Cameron, physician, and martyr to the Stewart cause; Cameron of Fassifern, the hero of Quatre Bras; and always inseparable from these – the Cameron men!

There are several historic lochs in Lochaber. There is lonely Loch Treig, surrounded by precipitous hills rising sheer from the water, and at one end an islet called the Council Island.

Many a time have the Camerons convoyed their Chief to the loch when he went on the island to confer with the Mackintosh over some Clan dispute. It was selected as the meeting-place because there the two chiefs could be alone with no risk of being ambushed. On the hillside and overhanging the loch is a huge boulder called the Watch Rock, from which Cameron sentinels could keep an eye on the welfare of their Chief!

More lonely still is the little Loch of the Swords where an old-standing boundary dispute was settled between Lochiel and Murray of Atholl. The whole beautiful region abounds in Clan memories. Little wonder if Camerons in foreign countries should be homesick for the sight of it! It is said that during the wars abroad the pipers had actually to be forbidden to play the old tune, *Farewell to Lochaber*, because of its depressing effect on the spirits of the Cameron Highlanders. But homesickness soon disappeared when it came to fighting, for then the enemy found himself faced by men who did not know the meaning of the word 'defeat'.

Most people know Fort William as it is to-day. It was built in Cromwell's time, and used as a fort. It was, in fact, the headquarters of the English troops that were sent to keep the Camerons in order. Long after the other Clans had given in, they stood out, and many a fierce skirmish they had with the Sassenachs. There was one occasion when Lochiel and his clansmen were in a very tight corner indeed! They had been defending one end of a mountain pass, when they found themselves being attacked from the other end as well! Capture seemed to stare them in the face – but they were not done yet! Slowly and in regular formation they retreated – up the steep mountain-side. Facing their enemies they stepped – back and up, back and up, in perfect order! The hillsides were deep with snow, and the Englishmen, unused to such ground, did not dare to follow. They could only watch, and gasp with amazement and unwilling admiration, when at last the gallant band, still facing them, disappeared from view over the high hilltop!

The Highland soldiers were inured to all sorts of hardships. It is told that the fighting father of Cameron sons considered himself disgraced one night during this campaign, when sleeping out in the snow with his company.

This Cameron saw one of his sons make a large snowball for a pillow, and, full of contempt, he got up and kicked it away, saying, 'Are you become so like a woman that you cannot sleep without such luxury?'

Following the lead of their Chief the Camerons were always devoted adherents of the Stewarts. They fought at Killiecrankie, where Lochiel's counsel to 'fight immediately while the men were in good heart' prevailed, and justified itself.

At the Jacobite Rebellion of 1715 Sir Ewan Cameron was an old man, but his son, Allan, attended the Chevalier when he came from France to take part in the campaign. A curious incident happened at this time. Very early on the morning on which the Chevalier de St George (son of James II) landed at Peterhead, Sir Ewan started from his sleep and called out to Lady Cameron, 'Wife, wife! The King has landed! The King has landed, – and our son Allan is with him!'

Lady Cameron told him he had been dreaming, but he repeated his words, and, rising in haste, he roused the household and commanded a large bonfire to be built.

Then the best liquor in the house had to be brought out so that all his 'lads' – as he called his clansmen – and friends might be able to drink the King's health. His lady said that he was very foolish to make all these preparations because of a dream, but he was so urgent and gave such definite commands that, against her own judgment, she was inspired to fall in with his mood, and help with a will in the great doings. All the people in the neighbourhood were commanded to the festivity, which sent on – Highland fashion – for two days. News took long to travel then, but, before many days, definite tidings reached Lochaber to confirm the fact that the day and the hour of the arrival of the Prince and his attendants (among whom was Allan Cameron) exactly coincided with Sir Ewan's announcement to his wife!

When Prince Charlie landed in Scotland, Sir Ewan's grandson, Donald – called the 'Gentle Lochiel' – was one of the first nobles summoned to meet him. Lochiel knew quite well that the Jacobite cause was a forlorn hope, for Charles had neither money nor resources; and he begged the Prince to wait until he had some more definite support. But the Prince was impatient with this wise counsel and he exclaimed angrily, 'In a few days, with the few friends that I have, I will erect the Royal Standard and proclaim to the people of Britain that Charles Stuart has come over to claim the crown of his ancestors. And Lochiel may stay at home, and from the newspapers learn the fate of his Prince!' But Lochiel exclaimed, 'No! I'll share the fate of my Prince, and so shall every man over whom Nature or Fortune has given me any power!' When Charles with only a hundred and fifty followers went to erect his standard at Loch Shiel in Glen Finnan, he found the place quiet and deserted, and his spirits were low indeed. But by and by there came the distant sound of pipes, and soon the notes of a Cameron pibroch, accompanied by the regular tramp of feet were borne on the wind towards him. Then over the crest of a hill appeared a line of tartan. The line became a glowing mass which spread down over the hillside, drawing nearer in regular formation. It was the Cameron Men, nearly eight hundred strong! Then, and only then, the Prince gave his banner to the Marquis of Tullibardine to unfurl – and so began the great 'Rising of the 'Forty-five'!

Lochiel fulfilled his promise to Prince Charlie nobly and unsparingly. In his service he gave all – home, health and liberty. He was wounded in both ankles at Culloden. Along with the Prince he hid in his own woods of Achnacarry, in a cave in the neighbourhood, in Cluny Macpherson's Cage on Ben Alder. Later he accompanied Prince Charlie to France, but he died there in the year 1748.

Dr Archibald Cameron, brother of the Gentle Lochiel, was another to suffer in the Stewart cause. He escaped to France, but returning to Scotland on various missions he was caught at last. He was the last Jacobite to pay the extreme penalty.

In later days one of the most distinguished members of the Clan was Captain John Cameron of Fassifern. An able and brilliant soldier, his military career was cut short during the Napoleonic Wars at Quatre Bras in 1815, when, at the command of the Duke of Wellington, he led his regiment, the famous 92nd, in a glorious charge, in which, alas! he was mortally wounded. 'How goes the day?' he asked anxiously, and when told, 'All's well,' he said, 'I die happy, and I trust my dear country will believe I have served her faithfully.'

The charge of the 92nd at Quatre Bras has been the subject of many patriotic poems, one of the best known being that of Professor Blackie, which finishes with the verse:

'And now he sleeps – for they bore him home
When the war was done, across the foam –
Beneath the shadow of Nevis Ben
With his sires, the pride of the Cameron men.
As they laid him to rest on his native ground;
The Cameron brave, whose eyes never
    quailed,
Whose heart never sank, and whose hand
    never failed,
When the Cameron men were wanted!'

6

Clan MacGregor

Nameless by Day!

THE ill-fated Clan Alpin or MacGregor claims descent
from an early Scottish King, called Kenneth Alpin. So
the MacGregors adopted as their motto the Gaelic
words 'S'rioghal mo dhream' ('Royal is my race').
Because of an adventure of one of their early chiefs the
motto was changed later to 'E'en do and spare not!'

In days when wild boars were common in Scotland
a MacGregor went out to attend his King on a hunting
expedition. An enormous wild boar was encountered
and the King pursued it. But it happened that he was
no match for that particular boar and instead of
attacking he found himself attacked! MacGregor had
no wish to spoil sport, but he saw that the King was in
danger and he called out to ask whether he should
help him, getting the prompt answer, 'E'en do and
spare not!' And the story goes that MacGregor tore up
a young oak-tree by the roots and used it in his left
hand to keep off the infuriated animal until he got a
chance to kill it with his sword; and after that incident
the King's words were used as the MacGregor motto.

The shield in the MacGregor coat-of-arms shows the oak-tree, with a sword across it, which bears on its point a crown – to show that it was used in a king's service.

In the eleventh century the MacGregors were a flourishing Clan and a knighthood was given to their Chief, while his son was made Abbot of Dunkeld. Then they became Lords of Glenorchy, and were an important Highland family. While Robert the Bruce was struggling for the independence of Scotland, the MacGregors were his loyal supporters. They sheltered Bruce in a cave on Loch Lomond side until they could get him taken across the Loch and conveyed from there to his own part of the country. The east side of Loch Lomond was one of the boundaries of the wide MacGregor country. It was well guarded by great mountains and deep forests; so the Clan was able to settle in kindly valleys, safe from marauders, and out of reach of the laws and forces of the Scots Government.

Their fortunes took an evil turn, and the cause was surely the strangest that ever brought about the downfall of a great family. It was – a black sheep with a white tail! In the sixteenth century two MacGregors found themselves in the Colquhoun country, which lies at Luss, on the west bank of the Loch Lomond. It was nightfall and they were tired and hungry. It is said that they asked for hospitality at Luss and were refused, which is a very unusual thing in the Highlands! So, because they were angry as well as hungry, they killed and roasted a black sheep with a white tail. Then they ate their supper and spent the night in a tumble-down barn near Luss. In the morning, of course, the sheep was missed, and its skin was found in the barn beside the two MacGregors. The Colquhouns were so enraged that they hanged both men; and so began a Clan feud which lasted for nearly a century. Then the Chief of the MacGregors thought it was time to stop the bickering which continually went on, and he went with a following to Luss – to propose peace. But his mission had no result, so the MacGregors took the road for home. The Luss men followed and caught them up at a lonely glen where a terrible fight took place.

The MacGregors were the victors. Over two hundred Colquhouns were killed. The glen is known as Glen Fruin – the Glen of Weeping.

The Laird of Luss, furious at his defeat, sent a very unfair account of the business to the King. His messenger was accompanied by a procession of widows of the slain Colquhouns, each one mounted on a white pony and carrying her husband's bloodstained shirt on the point of a lance. Naturally this parade made a great impression at Stirling, and there was no one about the Court to plead the cause of the MacGregors and urge that the quarrel had not been of their seeking. The Privy Council ordered that the name of MacGregor should be abolished, and that any who continued to bear it should be put to the sword. The Earl of Argyll was given authority to hunt and persecute the Clan. Many MacGregors were killed, and their lands were seized and given to other Clans. And many went to different parts of the country and took other names. But nothing could break the *spirit* of the Clan! At last a champion arose among them who thought that he might avenge their wrongs. This was Robert MacGregor Campbell, or Rob Roy, a man of good descent. He was a successful cattle drover who did good business at the Lowland and Border fairs. The Duke of Montrose advanced a good deal of money to him to invest in cattle. Unfortunately Rob Roy had a dishonest partner who made off with his money, as well as £1000 belonging to the Duke, and left Rob to take the blame. The Duke demanded his money back, but Rob had no hope of finding £1000! In his predicament he did the worst possible thing, for he took to flight. Then the Duke had his property seized and a warrant issued for his arrest. And from that time onward his life was that of an outlaw, and his daring escapades were the talk of the whole of Britain.

He had many hiding-places. One of them was the very same cave which, four hundred years before, had sheltered Robert the Bruce. Another was a cavern in a mass of rock which rises from Loch Lomond. It is called Rob Roy's Prison, because he used to keep captives there from whom he hoped to extort ransom.

His way of dealing with his prisoners was to lower them into the Loch by a rope, and between dips to ask them whether they were ready to agree to his terms! Several times he was himself captured. Once the Duke of Atholl decoyed him (under pretence of friendship) to his castle, and there Rob was handed over to an officer and sixty soldiers. He let himself be taken quietly, but he made a request that he should be allowed to send a message to his wife. A mounted messenger came to get the message and Rob asked him to dismount, that he might give it to him privately. Unsuspecting, the man got off his horse and Rob began to speak confidentially to him, edging gradually towards the door. Then suddenly he made a spring, and was up, and *off* before anyone could stop him! Another time he was surprised and taken prisoner by the Duke of Montrose, and was bound on a horse behind one of the Duke's followers. It was late evening and growing dark when they reached the River Forth. As they were crossing it the buckle of the girth which bound him slipped, and down Rob dropped into the water and swam for safety, easily getting away in the dark. You can imagine how angry Montrose was when the luckless follower arrived at the river bank without his prisoner!

After many years of wild adventures and amazing escapes Rob Roy settled down to a more or less peaceful life. The Duke of Montrose became less hard on the MacGregors and even began to lease land to them, and Rob went to Balquhidder and settled down to farming. But his proud spirit was never broken – as Sir Walter Scott in his introduction to his novel, *Rob Roy*, tells. He says: 'When he was old and ill he was told that a man with whom he had been at enmity in old days was coming to visit him. His pride rose in arms and he said, 'Raise me from my bed, throw my plaid round me and bring me my claymore, dirk and pistols. It shall never be said that a foeman saw Rob Roy defenceless and unarmed!' The visitor entering asked after Rob's health and Rob replied civilly though coolly. But as soon as the man had gone he fell back, completely exhausted with the effort. 'Now,' he said, 'all is over. Let the piper play *Ha til mi tulidh* ("We return no more").' Before the dirge was finished the great Rob Roy was dead.'

Late in the eighteenth century a law was passed allowing the MacGregors to use their name once more. There have been a great many distinguished sons of the Clan since then, and Sir Walter Scott's words have come true, that, after all their misfortunes, 'MacGregor, despite them, shall flourish for over!'

7

Clan Forbes

Culloden – for the King
Pitsligo – for the Prince

JOHN OF FORBES was the first of the Clan to be mentioned in Scottish records and that was in the days of William the Lion. Among his descendants was Sir John Forbes of that ilk, who lived in the reigns of Robert II and Robert III. He had four stalwart sons, and they founded the families of Forbes of Pitsligo, Waverton, and Foveran in Aberdeenshire, and of Culloden in Inverness-shire. James I raised the eldest of these sons to the Peerage as a reward for distinguished service in France.

A curious custom existed at that time by which a Peer could demand what was called a bond of *manrent* from a less powerful neighbour. This was a sort of personal bondage. It gave him the right to claim three armed horsemen as a bodyguard 'to shield him against all mortals, the King excepted', and this claim Lord Forbes made on the family of Ogston of that ilk. Lord Forbes' wife was the granddaughter of Robert III, so the Forbeses can boast of royal blood. His branch of the family added considerably to the honours and possessions of the Clan; and it has always been said that about one-third of the ancient castles in Aberdeenshire were either built by the Forbeses or were at one time owned by them. They were a sturdy race of fighters and saw to it that no one should defraud them of their rights and privileges.

John, the sixth Lord, had a feud with the city of Aberdeen. This town demanded blackmail of a tun of wine for the privilege of the fishings in the River Don, which ran through Forbes land. (A tun is a huge cask which holds 232 gallons). In 1526 a great fight between the Forbeses and the citizens of Aberdeen took place in the streets. It went on for twenty-four hours without break until both sides were completely exhausted.

The Forbeses of Tolquhoun – like their descendants of Culloden – were ever loyal to the reigning monarch. In the Scots array at the Battle of Worcester one of them commanded a troop of cavalry. When Charles II's horse was shot from under him and it was clear that the fight was going against him, Forbes mounted the King on his own horse, putting also his buff-coloured coat and bloodstained scarf upon the King. Disguised in this way, and surrounded by sixty Forbeses, Charles managed to evade capture, and at nightfall he got away to a safe place and thence to France.

The most famous descendant of this branch was Duncan Forbes of Culloden, the Lord President of the Court of Session. The Government was undoubtedly indebted to him for influencing the northern Highlands against joining the Rising of the ' 'Forty-five'. Apart from his loyalty to the Government, he wanted to prevent his friends and neighbours in the north from joining in a cause which he knew very well was doomed to fail. Whenever the news of the raising of Prince Charlie's standard reached him, he hurried to Inverness and used every means possible to keep the chiefs from going out. He advanced £2000 out of his own pocket for purposes of defence, and the ungrateful Government never repaid him! While he was acting in this way, one of his kindred in Aberdeenshire urged equally by conscience and by loyalty – loyalty to the ancient House of Stewart – decided to throw in his lot with Prince Charlie. This was Alex Forbes, Lord Pitsligo, who had always been a recognised leader among the east-country Jacobites. He had fought in the ' 'Fifteen', when Prince Charlie's father tried to gain the throne of Scotland. Then, when the next call came – thirty years later – he was an old man of sixty-seven and he naturally hesitated about taking up arms. But not for long! Like the 'Gentle Lochiel', he stood firm to the cause, and cheerfully sacrificing his fortunes, placed his life in peril, because of his personal attachment to the House of Stewart. After the defeat of Culloden, when he became an exile and a wanderer, he managed to find shelter in Buchan, a district of north-east Aberdeenshire, on the borders of his own estates. Pitsligo Castle (now a crumbling ruin) stands on rising ground on the north coast in bleak country, whose only attraction is its fine rocky coast-line, with – here and there – lovely little sandy bays. Among the rocks near the castle is a cave which was Lord Pitsligo's hiding-place for some years. In a rough recess at its farther end on a shelf of rock dried bracken was laid to serve as a bed. Whenever it was safe to do so, his friends brought him food, but he was often reduced to feeding on water-brose – which is just oatmeal moistened with water. He had a few books and they were his only distraction fiom the cries of the seabirds and the roar of the waves upon the rocky shore. Sometimes he went about the country disguised as a beggar. Lady Pitsligo used to sew bags for him with which to go about collecting meal and broken meats. Another hiding-place was under the arch of a small bridge near Fraserbugh. Sometimes he was taken by surprise. On one occasion a patrol of soldiers came upon him near Rosehearty and, taking him for a genuine beggar, commanded him to 'take them to the cave where Lord Pitsligo was in hiding!' He could not help himself and he led them to his own rocky cavern. He was amused at the precautions they took to avoid warning its hoped-for occupant. They tiptoed among the rocks, and bursting into the cave shouted, 'In the King's name, surrender!' But only the echoes answered: and the seabirds, indignant at the intruders, screamed shrilly, and attacked their faces with wings and beaks, so that the soldiers had to retreat. Owing to the cold and exposure, Lord Pitsligo became a victim to asthma. One day he had a bad fit of coughing at the roadside, during which a patrol passed. So little did the soldiers suspect him that one of them stopped and sympathised with him and even gave him a small sum of money!

In this way his life went on for ten long years, and meanwhile his title and estates had been forfeited by law. His last escape was a very strange one. A rumour had reached the commanding officer in Fraserburgh that the old man was hiding a few miles away in the House of Auchiries, where his son lived. A lady who was visiting in the house dreamed repeatedly one night that soldiers surrounded the house, and her dream was so persistent that she got up and looked out of the window. Dawn was just breaking, and to her amazement she saw soldiers posted round the house as she had seen them in her dream. She gave the alarm at once, and the family lost no time in transferring the old man from his bed to a recess behind the panelled walls of one of the bedrooms. A bed was placed against this panel and the lady who had dreamed lay down in it before the soldiers were admitted. They searched every corner of the house. the lady's bed was carefully examined, and the soldiers even felt her chin to make sure that she was not a man in a woman's nightgown! While they were doing this the stuffy air of the recess brought on poor Lord Pitsligo's cough, and his breathing became so loud that those in the house were terrified for his safety. But the lady was equal to the occasion. She coughed so loudly and violently herself that she succeeded in covering the noise which he made, and the soldiers departed discomfited. When Lord Pitsligo could speak after being released from his uncomfortable hiding-place, he said kindly to his servant – 'James, go and see that those poor fellows get some breakfast and a drink of warm ale. It is a cold morning and they are only doing their duty.' And he added with a smile, 'A poor prize, had they got me – an old dying man!' No further attempt was made to seize him and he lived on with his son until the age of eighty-five.

The Forbeses may well be proud of this clansman of theirs, for his character was worthy of remembrance. It was said of him by a great man of his day: 'I have never heard this gentleman speak an ill word of any man living; but I have always observed him ready to defend any other person who was ill spoken of in his company. My Lord Pitsligo will always find good in everybody.' Aytoun's ballad rightly calls him:

'The good old Scottish Cavalier
All of the olden time.'

8

Clan Menzies

AMONG those families which were not originally Highland, but have won both power and positon in the Highlands, is that of Menzies.

The clansfolk are of Celtic stock, but the head of the family is generally believed to have come over from Normandy with William the Conqueror, and to have the same root as the English family of Manners, of the Rutland dukedom. The name was then 'de Menyers', and so it was written in early Scottish records, when the family seat was at Durisdeer in Nithsdale. Since that time it has been spelt in many different ways. The reason for introducing Z into its present form has always been a puzzle, but a possible clue is given in the *Red and White Book of Menzies*.

In ancient times, when scarcely anybody but the monks could read and write, all letters and documents were written by professional scribes. The letter Z in Latin writing was so remarkably like the Celtic G that it is probable that the writer of some important document used it in error. There would be no one to correct the mistake, and the spelling would be repeated in succeeding documents as MENZIES. That, of course, would not affect the pronunciation which has always been 'Mingis'. Whether correct or not, that is the theory of the Menzies Chronicler.

The Menzieses of the thirteenth century were a very able family. In 1249 Lord Robert de Menyers was Lord High Chancellor of Scotland. He was often sent on embassies to the English Court, and his conduct of affairs was of great advantage to both nations. In his time Scotland made great progress in Commerce, Literature and the Arts. His son got a grant of the lands of Weem, Aberfeldy, and Glendochart from Robert the Bruce; and his grandson was given land in Fortingall by Robert II. His family must always have been in favour with royalty, for grants of land to different branches were given, in counties as far apart as Peebles, Lothian and Aberdeen – where they took a prominent part in civic government.

In the sixteenth century the Menzieses came into serious conflict with their Highland neighbours. After three generations there was no male heir to Fortingall and the estate went to the Stewarts, by marriage with the Menzies heiress. Then Menzies of Weem laid claim to the lands of Rannoch and was granted a charter of them by James IV. The very day the charter was signed, the wild men of Rannoch descended upon Weem. They were led by Neil Stewart, a kinsman of the Menzieses by marriage; and besides doing a great deal of damage they burned down Castle Weem. Such an affront had, of course, to be avenged, so the Menzieses in full force promptly burned down Stewart's Castle of Garth! Apart from the destruction of two fine old castles, the loss to the Menzies family was very great, because with Castle Weem were burnt the early records of their origin, besides several important royal charters. To judge from the stories that have been passed on by word of mouth in Perthshire it would seem that the Menzies chiefs were settled at Weem much earlier than is shown by existing history. There is an ancient Gaelic ballad about an ogre who in very early ages lived in a cave – or Pict's house – at

Weem. He went about in the guise of a monk with a scarlet cowl, and his fierce and repulsive appearance terrified the whole neighbourhood. One day he met the daughter of the Menzies Chief. She was a girl of great beauty and 'His Ogreship' determined to have her for his bride. She fled from him in horror, but he accomplished his fell purpose and carried her off to his cave. She was never seen again!

A belief exists among the Clan that Crinan, Abbot of Dunkeld, was a Menzies chief. He married the daughter of King Malcolm II, and their son Duncan became King of Scotland. Duncan was assassinated by Macbeth, Thane of Cawdor, who usurped the crown and occupied the throne of Scotland for seventeen years. Everybody knows the story of Macbeth consulting three witches as to his prospects, and how they told him that until Birnam Wood should come to Dunsinane he should never be conquered or lose his crown. In time Duncan's son, Malcolm, came to manhood, and he raised an army to attack Macbeth and avenge his father. This army (which included Menzieses in full strength) spent the night before the attack in Birnam Woods. Early in the morning Malcolm ordered that every man should hew down a branch and bear it before him on the march to Dunsinane, where Macbeth's stronghold was. So hidden, the strength of his army could not possibly be estimated by the enemy in the fort. When told by a sentinel of the strange appearance of the advancing wood, Macbeth wrathfully refused to believe him. But 'seeing is believing' and Macbeth's incredulity was changed to terror when he realised that his doom was about to overtake him – as indeed turned out to be the case! Malcolm's success in this battle restored the old royal line of Scotland, which lasted without a break for hundreds of years. In the advance on Birnam Wood the Menzieses carried branches of the rowan (or mountain-ash) which, ever since, has been the Clan badge. Their hunting tartan also repeats the colours of the rowan-tree – green for the leaves and scarlet for the berries.

Another tree which will always be associated with a Menzies is the larch; for, from the Austrian Tyrol, Menzies of Culdares brought in his portmanteau the first larches ever planted in Scotland. This was in 1737. The Duke of Atholl of that time was a skilful and enthusiastic gardener – he was called 'The Planting Duke'. Menzies presented the Duke with some of the young larches and they were planted at Dunkeld. Two of them can be seen – now grown to monstrous size – beside Dunkeld Cathedral. They proved to be ideally suitable for the Scottish climate and soil, and seedlings were begged – or even stolen – by gardeners from all over the kingdom.

At Castle Menzies there are some of the finest trees in all Scotland. When Prince Charlie's father came to Britain in 1715 to make a bid for the throne of Scotland, the Menzieses were among the Clans which rallied to his call – as the following verse of a poem by Campbell tells:

> 'Wha' will ride wi' gallant Murray?
> Wha' will ride wi' Geordie's sel'?
> He's the flow'r o' a' Glenisla
> An' the darling o' Dunkell!
> *Menzies*, he's our friend and brother,
> Gask and Strowan are nae slack;
> Noble Perth has ta'en the field,
> And a' the Drummonds at his back!'

But, as you know, this rising ended in failure. When, thirty years later, the attractive – but just as unfortunate – Stewart Prince Charles Edward came over on the same errand as his father, Menzies of Culdares did not himself turn out; but his clansmen did, under Menzies of Shian. Prince Charlie spent two happy days at Castle Menzies, not long before his mission failed on the field of Culloden. He had some good hunting and, for the time, cast all his cares to the winds of Perthshire.

Although Menzies did not join the Rising, he showed his sympathy by sending a very handsome charger to the Prince for his own use. The horse was taken by one of the clansmen and was to be handed over to Prince Charlie who was then in England. But on the way south both man and horse were captured by Government troops. The man was pressed to reveal the name of the sender of the horse, and was told that, if he did, he should go free. But the loyal Highlander would not betray his chief; he preferred – and suffered – death, which was the only alternative offered him.

Ben Lawers, one of the highest Perthshire mountains, is partly on Weem territory. It is a very beautiful hill and on it are found many rare plants. A story is told of a St Andrews professor who wanted to climb the mountain. He asked the Menzies Chief to give him an escort for that purpose, and a gillie was told off to show the way. As they ascended the mountain the professor exclaimed – loud and often – at the rare plants, the glorious views, the fine air, and what not – until the gillie was thoroughly tired of his companion's enthusiasm. At last they reached the summit and, as the professor's eyes travelled from one range of mountains to another, he exclaimed in delight, 'Isn't this *marvellous*! Tell me, have any living beings ever been here before?' And the gillie dourly said, 'Oh, well indeed, sir, there's plenty goats come up Ben Lawers.' That day, it is said, a quiet and thoughtful professor went down Ben Lawers!

9

Clan Mackintosh

THE Gaelic word t-o-s-i-c-h ('tosh') means thane or earl, and some historians say that the first Mackintosh was the son of MacDuff, Thane or Earl of Fife.

For centuries Clan Mackintosh was prominent in the north-east Highlands, and when the Chief became the acknowledged captain of Clan Chattan as well, its importance was greatly enhanced.

The family seat of the Mackintosh is Moy Hall, on the banks of Loch Moy in Inverness-shire. There have been no fewer than three castles in the loch; the second – which for a short time sheltered Prince Charlie – was burnt down; and the third – where King George sometimes visited – was built in the eighteenth century.

Clan Chattan was the name of a combine of nine or ten Clans, which in early times banded themselves together in order to keep a grip of the north-east counties. The two leading Clans in this combine were

Mackintosh and Macpherson, and there was between these two a good deal of rivalry.

But the members of Clan Chattan were just like the members of some large family. They might – and *did* – quarrel among themselves, but if an outsider began to make trouble with any one of them the rest at once rose in his defence.

For example, Mackintosh of Moy had come to loggerheads with an old enemy, Macdonald of Keppoch. In a fierce fight at Mulroy the Moy men had the worst of it, and their Chief was taken prisoner.

That was a black day for the Mackintosh!

But before the Macdonalds could collect their scattered forces, warpipes were heard, and, to their dismay, a large body of Macphersons appeared in full battle array. They sent a message to Macdonald that, unless he was prepared for another fight, he must deliver up the Mackintosh at once!

A *second* battle in one day! Alas! No! Not even the Macdonalds could face that, so ruefully they had to hand over their prize. And the Macphersons, in triumph, escorted the Mackintosh Chief back to his estate of Moy!

Clan Comyn also had an old-standing feud with the Mackintoshes. On one occasion this Clan managed to drive the Mackintoshes to take refuge on the Island of Moy, and afterwards started making a dam, so as to raise the level of the loch and flood the island.

The Mackintoshes would certainly have been drowned had not one of their number gone down at dead of night and bored a number of holes in the wood which lined the dam. In each hole he placed a plug with a string attached, then all the strings were fastened to one rope. When everything was ready the Mackintoshes gave the main rope a mighty pull, and out came all the plugs!

The banked-up water poured through the holes with a fearful force, carrying away the wood, the turf which banked it up, *and* the Comyns who were encamped behind it!

For a long time the Chiefs of Mackintosh were associated with a dreadful curse. The story is told in an old poem called *The Curse of Moy*. A Mackintosh Chief wanted to marry Margaret, daughter of a Grant

Chief. Margaret refused his proposal because she was already engaged to Grant of Alva – and great was the affront to the Mackintosh! But he was determined not to be baulked, and he captured not only the lady, but her father and lover as well, and imprisoned all three in the island castle. Poor Margaret wept, and begged for mercy from her captor, who agreed to spare *one* of his prisoners, leaving her to choose which should die!

Margaret's father prevailed upon her to choose her lover's freedom, but that did not please Mackintosh at all, and in his rage he killed both men, and confronted the poor girl with their bodies! the poem tells how she went out of her mind, and for years roamed about the Badenoch mountains.

Over a cairn built in memory of her father and her lover she called down a curse on their murderer, praying that he might die childless:

'That never the son of a Chief of Moy
Might live to protect his father's age,
Or close in peace his dying eye,
Or gather his gloomy heritage.'

And superstitious folks looked upon it as a fulfilment of the curse, that for over a hundred years no Chief of Mackintosh left a son to succeed him. But with Angus, the twenty-fifth Chief, the spell was broken, for his son and his grandson in turn became Chief of the Clan.

In reading the history of any of the great Clans, one sees them constantly striving for supremacy over their powerful neighbours. The Mackintoshes, for instance, had to keep a watchful eye on Moray and Banffshire. Even far-away Ross-shire held possible enemies.

One of the worst Clan fights on record took place between the Mackintoshes and the Munros of Foulis, over the division of plunder taken by the Munros from a Perthshire Clan. They met at Clachnaharry, near Inverness, and scarcely any of the combatants were left to tell the tale!

Soon after William, the sixth Chief, became head of the Clan he was involved in the renewal of an old family quarrel with the Marquis of Huntly.

How it originated we do not know, but at this time young Mackintosh burned down the Castle of

Auchindown. Huntly marched against him, and a fierce battle ensued in which William was taken prisoner. He was tried in Aberdeen, and condemned to death by a Court selected by Huntly.

The only man who dared to protest was Menzies, Provost of Aberdeen, and he was so incensed by the unfairness of the trial that he announced his intention of reporting it to Parliament. Even Huntly did not dare to proceed with the sentence, but he sent Mackintosh to the care of Lady Huntly at his Castle of Strathbogie.

The young man appealed to her for justice, and (according to Sir Walter Scott) she replied to him, 'Mackintosh, you have offended Huntly so deeply that he has sworn that he will never pardon you until he has brought your neck to the block.'

This interview took place in the kitchen of Strathbogie and William loosened his collar, and laid his head on the wooden block on which cattle and sheep were broken up, saying, as he did so, 'Even to that humiliation I will stoop, to secure the safety of my father's house!' A generous-hearted woman would have been touched by such submission, but not so the Marchioness! She made a sign to the cook, who was standing near with a meat chopper in his hand, and he raised it and struck off the young man's head!

Another – but very different – woman to bear a share in Clan affairs was Lady Mackintosh at the time of the ' 'Forty-five'.

Although only twenty at the time, she was so active in Prince Charlie's service that she became known as 'Colonel Anne'. Her husband was out on the Government side with Loudon's Highlanders, but she was a Farquharson of Invercauld and therefore a devoted Jacobite. In order to help the Prince she roused her husband's Clan to sympathetic action, and a strong, well-armed battalion was formed. On the battalion's first appearance 'Colonel Anne' reviewed them, with a man's bonnet on her head, a tartan riding-habit, and pistols at her saddle-bow!

In February 1746 – just after visiting Menzies at Weem Castle – Prince Charlie came to Moy. The night he arrived, Lady Mackintosh sent out the blacksmith of Moy, with four other men, to guard the approach from

Inverness against sudden alarm. It was a wild night of thunder and lightning and the scouts took up position beside a number of peat-stacks which were drying on both sides of the road. Presently they heard approaching the regular tramp of marching troops. They were five men against hundreds – what could they do? When the soldiers came near the blacksmith and his men began rushing about among the peat-stacks, firing their guns and shouting loudly the war-cries of Lochiel, Keppoch, and other well-known Jacobite Clans.

The lightning lit up the peat-stacks, which to the soldiers looked like bodies of men in formation, and they thought that the Jacobite army was upon them in full strength. They hesitated, broke, and fled back to Inverness as hard as they could go! And so ended what is known as the 'Rout of Moy'.

The gallant smith was ever after known as 'Captein nan Coig' ('Captain of the Five'). He was made an officer in the Mackintosh Regiment, and his sword was preserved in the district. His anvil is now at Moy Hall, along with several relics of Prince Charlie.

After Culloden, a party of Government soldiers was sent to bring Lady Mackintosh to Inverness. Mounted on the only horse left at Moy she rode with them, undaunted and unconcerned. She was kept under guard for six weeks and afterwards set at liberty.

Some years later, at a ball given by the Duke of Cumberland in London, the first tune played was *Up and waur them a', Willie*. It was the tune which was played by the bells of St Giles, when the Duke passed through Edinburgh on his way to the Highlands, to suppress the Prince Charlie Rising.

To this tune the Duke invited Lady Mackintosh to dance and she could not refuse her host. The dance finished, she said, 'Well, sir, I have danced to your tune. Will you now dance to mine?'

Being always gallant the Duke could not say, 'No'; but the victor of Culloden must have felt himself in rather a ridiculous position when he found that the tune which the lady called, and to which he had to dance, was, *The Auld Stuarts back again!* So the final honour in that skirmish went unquestionably to gallant 'Colonel Anne'!

10

Clan Munro

THERE is some uncertainty as to the early home of the Clan Munro – or Clan Roich, as it is in the Gaelic. Some writers say that the Munros came from Ireland in far back ages; that they are descended from Donald O'Ceann, son of the Prince of Fermanagh, who came over to help Malcolm II against Danish invaders; and that Donald's reward was the land to the north-west of the Cromarty Firth which is still known as 'Ferin-Donald' ('the Land of Donald'). They say also that the name 'Munro' was taken from a river in County Derry called the Roe, and that Foulis (the name of the Munros' family seat) is derived from Loch Foyle, into which the Roe flows.

Whether this be true or not, the Munros have certainly owned their lands in Ross-shire for nearly eight hundred years. We know that they always kept on good terms with their great northern neighbours, the Earls of Sutherland and Ross, for very early in their history a Munro married the Earl of Sutherland's daughter. And, later, the family took a charter of land (they called it a Bond of Kindness and Alliance) from the Earl of Ross.

The land was granted to them on the curious condition that every year they should give the Earl of Ross a pair of white gloves, or three pennies, if required!

Loyalty to the Rosses led to an extraordinary loss in the Munro succession. In the time of Alexander III a rebellion broke out against the Earl of Ross. Its leader was seized and imprisoned at Dingwall, and, in revenge, the rebels went to the Ross Castle of Balnagown, and stole the Earl's son, holding him as a hostage against their imprisoned captain. Pursuit of the rebels by the Munros and Dingwalls ended in a dreadful fight, and although the Ross supporters won, their losses in men were very heavy.

Actually eleven Munros of the House of Foulis — who would naturally have succeeded in turn — fell, so that the only heir left was an infant then in its cradle. But the Earl's son was rescued and borne back in triumph to Balnagown, and that strengthened the good feeling already existing between the Rosses and the Munros.

In the fourteenth century John Munro of Foulis was travelling from Edinburgh to Ross-shire. On the way he and his retinue stopped for a night's rest in a meadow at Strathardle in Perthshire. While they were sleeping, the owner of the meadow came and cut off the tails of their horses.

Such an insult was bound to be avenged as soon as possible, so when Munro reached Foulis, he at once summoned is kinsmen and followers and organised a raid on the offenders. He returned with a large party to Strathardle, and killed some of the inhabitants and drove away their best cattle.

As the victorious party passed through Moy on their way home, the Mackintosh sent a message to Munro demanding *his* share of the spoil. The payment of what was called a 'Road Collop' for the liberty of driving plundered cattle through another chief's land was a regular Highland custom, and the Munros offered what they thought was a generous share.. But the

Mackintosh demanded a half-share and this the Munros refused and went on their way. The Mackintoshes pursuing them overtook them at Clachnaharry, near Inverness, where one of the worst Clan fights on record took place; in fact both sides were almost wiped out!

Euphemia, daughter of the Earl of Ross, was the wife of Robert II, and when the eighth Laird of Foulis married her niece, the Munros became vassals of the Crown. To hold land from a king raised the rank of a family. The ceremony itself was very quiet. When the vassal went into the King's presence, he fell on his knees and put his hands into the royal hands, the King then kissing him on the mouth. At the same time the Munro took an oath that he would be the King's faithful vassal all his life; and a charter was then granted to show that, for all time coming, certain lands would belong to him and his successors. In the charter granted by King Robert to the Munros there was only one condition — that in return for their lands they should produce for the King a *snowball* at midsummer! Foulis Castle lies just below Ben Wyvis in Ross-shire, and on the northern side of that massive mountain are corries where the snow never melts, so a 'snowball rent' even at midsummer was easy to pay!

In the reign of James VI, Lord Reay and Sir Robert Munro — commonly called 'The Black Baron' — were the first chiefs to seek military glory in foreign service.

Munro raised a regiment seven hundred strong among his own people, and fought, first for the King of Denmark and later for Prince Gustavus Adolphus of Sweden.

At one time there were in the Swedish army no fewer than fifty-seven officers of the name of Munro, not counting subalterns.

The military connection of the Clan was extended to India, where several Munros gained honour and renown. But India took an ungrateful toll of them, for two, at least, came to an untimely end — one being killed by a tiger and another devoured by a shark!

In addition to military distinction the Munros have achieved great things in Statesmanship, and in Literature, Law and Medicine.

Fifteen years after the Chair of Anatomy was founded in Edinburgh University three Monros in succession held the professorship for the long period of 126 years. The earliest of these (who was always spoken of as 'Monro Primus') distinguished himself at the Battle of Prestonpans, not as a slayer but as a healer. He attended to the wounded on both sides, and organised what was really an ambulance corps, to get the wounded taken to Edinburgh for treatment.

He made an interesting bargain with the Edinburgh Town Council which, at that time, appointed the professors. He offered to send his son to be trained at the best medical schools, both at home and abroad, if they would promise to appoint him Professor of Anatomy afterwards. And they had such faith in the father that they agreed to accept the son.

When the young man was fully qualified, he returned to Edinburgh and Monro Primus invited the City dignitaries to come and listen to his son's first lecture.

Monro Secundus had got it off by heart, but when he found himself faced by such a distinguished audience the poor fellow suddenly lost his nerve and forgot every word of the lecture! But when he had got over his first fright he pulled himself together, and, knowing his subject so thoroughly, he made a most brilliant oration and justified the faith of the Council. After this experience he never used notes for his lectures during the fifty-four years of his term as Professor of Anatomy. He was succeeded in turn by his son, Monro Tertius.

There is a story told about a Munro of Achany – a Sutherland branch of the Clan. The Earl of Sutherland, early one autumn, issued a commission to William Munro of Achany in Sutherlandshire, who with a large body of retainers and clansmen made a descent on Assynt and carried off a great many cattle. At the end of the summer, milk being plentiful, big supplies of butter and cheese had been made and laid in for winter use. So the Munros, not content with the cattle, made a clean sweep, and plundered the shielings of great quantities of butter and cheese as well! Assynt at one time belonged to Macleod of Lewis, but that family became extinct and the estate passed by marriage to the Mackenzies of Kintail.

In revenge for the raid of the Munros, a song was written and circulated by an Assynt farmer called Macleod, who set his words to the tune of *Caber Feidh*, the Clan March of the Mackenzies.

The song contained very bitter sarcasm about Sutherland and the Munros, who, in turn, were furious at the gibes in it, especially those about the butter and cheese. And Achany vowed that if he ever met the author of the song he would certainly kill him!

They were personally unknown to each other, but Achany was well known by a grey bonnet which he always wore — which had earned for him the name 'Uilleam a Bhonaid Aidhir' ('William of the Grey Bonnet').

One day he entered Ardgay Inn where sat Macleod, who was on his way to Tain Market, refreshing himself with bread and butter, cheese and ale. Macleod at once recognised the grey bonnet, and after the fashion of the day, rose and drank to the stranger, afterwards offering him the horn of ale in his turn. O the spur of the moment, he made up a Gaelic verse which he recited to Munro, and which, translated, ran something like this:

'Bread and butter and cheese for me
Ere death my mouth shall close.
And, traveller, there's a drink for thee
To please the Black Munros!'

Achany was gratified at this address and he quaffed the stranger's ale, and then asked his name. When told the name he was very much taken aback — but there! — he had drunk with the Macleod as his guest and he could do nothing but forgive him. And it is pleasant to record that the two were quite good friends ever after!

11

Robertson – Clan Donnachie

ACCORDING to a famous historian the Robertsons of Struan are the oldest family in Scotland, and the only remaining branch of the royal race which gave kings to the throne of Scotland during the eleventh and twelfth centuries.

The Clan was known from early times as Clan Donnachie, after a Chief called Donnachaidh Reamhar, or Duncan the Stout.

Robert the Bruce was very friendly with one of the Chiefs of Clan Donnachie, who, by request of the Bruce, took the name of Robert. The son of this chief did not use the Gaelic 'Mac', but was called 'Robert, Son of Robert', so the family name became Robertson. When a Clan was marching to battle, a standard-bearer carrying the Clan banner always led the way. One night when Clan Donnachie was on the way to Bannockburn to help Bruce, the Clan banner was as usual laid near its bearer on the ground. And when he

50

lifted the standard in the morning a precious stone which looked like a ball of milky crystal was found adhering to it. This incident was of course looked upon by Clan Donnachie as a sign that fortune would be with them in the fight. They called the stone 'Clach-nan-Brattich' – or 'Stone of the Banner' – and had it fixed to the top of the standard pole, and they never afterwards went into battle without it.

The Robertsons were always very loyal supporters of the Stewart kings. Indeed their crest is taken from an incident connected with James I of Scotland who was murdered in Blackfriars Monastery in Perth in the year 1451.

The Chief of the Clan followed the murderers and captured them in a lonely glen in Atholl. In recognition of this service his lands were made into a barony and to his coat-of-arms was added a crest which shows a hand and arm holding up a royal crown, and a savage in chains hanging from the shield. The motto granted to the Chief was 'Virtutis Gloria Merces' ('Glory is the reward of Valour'). One of the most famous of Robertson chiefs was Alexander, who was, almost certainly, the only chief in Scotland who was out in all three Jacobite Risings. In 1688, along with Graham of Claverhouse, he fought on the Stuart side, and had to take refuge in France. Queen Anne granted him a pardon and he returned to Scotland. Then came the Rising in 1715, when with five hundred of his clansmen he was at the Raising of the Standard on the Braes of Mar; he afterwards fought at Sheriffmuir. Twice he was taken prisoner and rescued; the second time, with the help of his sister, he escaped the Government soldiers and got away safely to France.

When the Rebellion of the ''Forty-five'' broke out he was seventy-five years old, but he insisted on joining his Clan and fighting for Prince Charlie at the Battle of Prestonpans. The Jacobite leaders, with some difficulty, persuaded him to go home and leave the rest of the fighting to the younger men.

Once persuaded, he must have quite enjoyed his journey, for it was made in a very grandly fitted-up carriage which had been captured from Sir John Cope. When the party reached the wilds of Rannoch, and the roads became too bad for carriage-wheels, the clansmen simply carried the carriage, their Chief within it, to his family residence, which was just below the great mountain Schiehallion. The old Highlanders must have been a sturdy race, for an old-fashioned carriage was no light weight!

Alexander Robertson was a scholar as well as a soldier. He was known as 'The Poet Chief', and after his death a volume of poems written by him was published. 'Baron Bradwardine', a character in Sir Walter Scott's novel, *Waverley*, is said to be a portrait of him. The talent for poetry was inherited by another of the race, for Baroness Nairne, the famous writer of many well-known Scots songs, was descended from the Robertsons of Struan. *The Auld Hoose*, one of her best-known songs, was written about the House of Gask, which belonged to her people. The old house became so dilapidated as to be unsafe and a new house was built close by into which the family moved. Lady Nairne's grandfather, Duncan Robertson of Struan, insisted that the last article taken from the old house to the new one should be the Family Bible, and he asked that he might have the honour of carrying it. Just as he had crossed the threshold with his precious burden the door of the 'Auld Hoose' burst its hinges and fell heavily outwards and the Chief had a very narrow escape!

For nearly five hundred years a branch of the Robertson family had a property in Perthshire called Lude. A greatly prized heirloom belonged to these Robertsons, who, like their Struan relatives, were keen supporters of the Stuarts. This was a harp which once belonged to Mary Queen of Scots.

The Queen stayed at Atholl in 1564, and an old record tells that a kind of competition amongst the native harpers was held in her honour. At this festival she adjudged the victory to Beatrix Gardyn of Banchory, to whom she gave her own harp as a prize. Beatrix Gardyn married one of the Robertsons of Lude and the harp was handed down in that family. Later it passed into the possession of a Stewart of Dalguise, and it was re-strung and actually played upon in the nineteenth century.

Music was an inherited talent among the Robertsons. Charles Robertson of Auchleeks (another connection) was so skilful a harper that he ws known all over Perthshire as 'Charles of the Strings'. He married Beatrix Robertson of Lude – a descendant of the Beatrix Gardyn to whom Queen Mary gave her harp. Music in Scotland is deeply indebted to a descendant of the Robertson family, for he founded the Chair of Music in Edinburgh University.

He was General John Reid, the son of Alexander Robertson of Straloch, whose forefathers for over three hundred years were always called Barons Rua, Roy, or Red, because the family had red hair. The head of the family always signed himself 'Robertson' until the General's time. He did not observe the rule, but kept the name and signature of 'Red', which he changed later on to 'Reid'. He had great taste for music and was one of the best flute-players of his time. When he was major in the 42nd Regiment he set the words of *The Garb of Old Gaul* to music, and this composition has ever since been the Regimental March. He left £52 000 for the purpose of establishing a Professorship of Music in the University of Edinburgh where he was educated. By his will he appointed that on or about the 13th of January (the date of his birthday) an annual concert should be held in the Hall of the Professor of Music and that the programme should commence with one of his compositions and include *The Garb of Old Gaul*. That was how the Reid Concerts began, and at the present day each January Concert opens with *The Garb of Old Gaul* and the audience rises to honour the memory of the man who did so much for music in Scotland.

Although Perth is the home county of Clan Donnachie many branches are settled in other counties – particularly in Aberdeenshire, Ross-shire and Lanarkshire and several variations of the name are found. These include Duncanson and MacRobbie. In Aberdeenshire some of the Clan took the name of Duncan, others that of MacConnachie, which was derived from Conan, the grandfather of Duncan the Stout.

The gathering-place of the Clan in olden times was the Fea Coire, a lonely glen behind the Rannoch Mountains.

12

Clan Gordon

THE Gordons are generally classed as a north country Clan because, for centuries, they have owned large tracts of land in the north-east of Scotland. But actually they had lands in Berwickshire and the Borders long before they settled in the north.

Some writers say that their ancestors came from France, from the village of Gourdon in Normandy.

The story is that the first Gordon to cross Tweed was a friend of Malcolm Canmore. He had the reputation of being a very valiant knight, and it is said that by his skill as a hunter he was able to rid Tweedside of a monstrous wild boar which had ravaged the whole district, killing many of the inhabitants. His bravery was rewarded by a grant of land in the district, and to commemorate his deed the boar's head was assumed as the armorial bearings of the family.

For three hundred years the Clan was closely connected with the history of the Borders. When the head of the family moved to the north the Gordons of Lochinvar and the Gordons of Earlston remained to carry on the name in the south of Scotland.

Early in their history a Gordon was killed while fighting in the Crusades. His grandson helped William Wallace to recapture the Castle of Wigton, of which he was made governor; and as a reward for his many faithful services. Robert the Bruce gave him a charter of the district of Strathbogie – or Huntly – in Aberdeenshire. It consisted of about a hundred and twenty square miles of land.

In 1388 the Earl of Douglas led a picked army into the north of England to fight the great Earl of Northumberland. There is an old ballad about the event which is called *The Battle of Otterbourne*, in which the name of the Gordons appears. The ballad begins:

'It fell about the Lammas tide
When the muir men win their hay,
The doughty Earl of Douglas rode
Into England to catch a prey.'

Then three clans specially chosen to help him are mentioned. It continues:

'*He chose the Gordons* and the Graemes,
With them the Lindsays light and gay –'

It is unnecessary to quote many stanzas, but later comes the following:

'The moon was clear, the day drew near,
The spears in flinders flew,
But mony a gallant Englishman
Ere day the Scotsmen slew.
The Gordons good in English blood
They steeped their hose and shoon.'

So the Gordons must have fought very lustily! But it was not only English blood that was spilt that moonlight night, for the leader of the Gordons was killed. His son, Sir Adam Gordon, it is related, gave his life for his country.

The great-grandson of the Otterbourne Gordon was created Earl of Huntly in recognition of his public service. Honour succeeded honour, for, some generations later, a descendant was made Marquis of Huntly; and the fourth Marquis became Duke of Gordon.

Two regiments called the Gordon Highlanders have been raised from this Clan, and both have earned the highest distinction in every war in which they have fought. When the second of these regiments was being raised, the Duchess of Gordon of that time had a method of her own for helping the recruiting. She promised that each recruit who took the King's shilling should have a kiss along with it; and a kiss from a beautiful duchess proved to be an irresistible inducement to the lads of the north-east!

In the sixteenth century one of the Gordons of Aboyne married Elizabeth, Countess of Sutherland. That established the name in the Highlands, for the Earls of Sutherland took the surname of Gordon and used it for more than two hundred years before they revived their old family name.

In East Aberdeenshire the Gordons are represented by the Earls of Aberdeen. Lord Byron, the poet, was descended from the Gordons of Gight in the same district. There are several branches of the Clan in Morayshire and the Laird of one of them was at one time a much-talked-of person. He was Sir Robert Gordon, and was known as the 'Warlock Laird of Moray'. He must have made a study of chemistry, because he had a laboratory in his house of Gordonstown, and it is said the queer old tools and crucibles and chemical apparatus that he used are still in existence. He was believed by the country folks to have uncanny powers, and stories are told about his weird doings. It was said that he had been trained as a sorcerer and that he had sold his shadow to the devil in payment of his knowledge of wizardry!

The Lairds of Gordonstown apparently found it convenient to be 'Not at Home' to callers at times, for in the old house there are several secret hiding-places which are very carefully arranged. One is gained by the removal in one of the roms of two planks, when a secret stair is disclosed, leading to a hidden room.

Another secret stair lead to the roof, and behind a cupboard is a recess large enough to hold half a dozen people.

A good deal of smuggling in those days went on in the north-east coast of Morayshire. It was not a particularly difficult matter because part of the coast is simply honeycombed with caves. One cave, which can be reached only at high tide, has the date 1650 on its walls. It is said to have been the smuggling stronghold of the Warlock Laird. He had a little brig called the *Nancy* and when a cargo of contraband goods was expected from France, her skipper used to watch for certain signals which told that she must be ready to take over from the French vessel. After the transfer, the goods were hidden in the cave until a high tide at night allowed of their safe removal. Another cave was used as a stable by a later Gordon of Gordonstown. In this cave he hid his horses in case they should be 'borrowed' by the Jacobite soldiers. Needless to say, once borrowed they were unlikely to be returned! Of the southern Gordons the Lochinvar branch was the best known. Sir Walter Scott wrote a poem which was possibly founded on a romantic incident in the Lochinvar family. A young Gordon in days of old was in love with the daughter of Graeme of Netherby in Cumberland. The young lady returned his affection, but her father refused to consider the offer of the young Scotsman and he arranged another marriage for her. Hearing at the last moment that the wedding day was fixed and the date close at hand, young Lochinvar rode off at full speed into England to try to stop it. But when he arrived at Netherby the wedding festivities were in full swing. Nothing daunted, he claimed the right to drink a cup of wine and tread the measure of a dance with the bride. However annoyed they might feel, neither her father, mother, nor bridegroom could refuse him the privilege. So the young couple danced together to the admiration of the assembled guests. Then:

'One touch to her hand, and one word in her
    ear,
When they reached the hall door and the
    charger stood near.

57

So light to the croupe the fair lady he swung,
So light to the saddle before her he sprung.
She is won! We are gone, over bank, bush and
    scaur!
'They'll have fleet steeds that follow,' quoth
    young Lochinvar!

There was mounting 'mong Graemes of the
    Netherby Clan,
Fosters, Fenwicks and Musgraves, they rode
    and they ran.
There was racing and chasing on Canonbie
    Lee,
But the lost bride of Netherby ne'er did they
    see!
So daring in love and so dauntless in war,
Have ye e'er heard of gallant like young
    Lochinvar?'

In the time of Charles I a member of the Lochinvar family was created Viscount Kenmure. This title was forfeited at the Stewart Rebellion of 1715. The Viscount Kenmure of that day was captured at the Battle of Preston, carried to London, tried, condemned and beheaded. On the scaffold he expressed regret that he had not thought of providing himself with a black suit so that he might have died with more decency! And before laying his head on the block he presented his executioner with eight guineas!

The greatest Gordon within living memory was Charles George Gordon, the hero of Khartoum. He joined the army in his youth and fought with distinction in the Crimean War. Six years later he put an end to a terrible rebellion which broke out in China. He commanded an army of British and Americans, and with them he won thirty-three battles in succession. He refused to take any reward for his services although the Emperor of China offered him enormous sums of money. Later, as Governor of the Egyptian Equatorial Provinces, he worked hard to put down the slave trade. In 1884, being the Governor of the Soudan, he returned after an absence of a few years to Khartoum, where he got an almost kingly welcome. The people, remembering him as a wise and kind ruler, thronged round him and bowed themselves to the sand before him. Had he not always been the champion of the slave? They were glad that he had come to protect them against the wild fanatical horde of Egyptians who had chosen as their leader the Mahdi, a man who supported the horrible practice of slavery. But the confidence of the people began to fail; for their enemies swarmed round the city, and instead of more soldiers being sent out from Britain to help Gordon, he was told to do the best he could, alone. It was hard enough to keep the enemy out, but when treachery crept into the city itself his task became a hopeless one, and he wrote the message:

If the expeditionary force does not come in ten days the town may fall, and I have done my best for the honour of our country.
Goodbye.
C. G. GORDON.

But relief did not come in ten days — nor even in forty! On a January night in 1885 a traitor in the pay of the enemy stole through the streets of Khartoum and opened one of the gates to let the Mahdi's forces in. With wild yells of triumph they surged into that doomed city and nothing could be done to stop them. At the first alarm, General Gordon appeared at the door of his house and was about to descend into the courtyard below, when he was struck by the enemy's bullets, and fell dead. At daybreak not a living man was left to defend the British flag which had flown there for so long and was now hauled down. Two days afterwards the relief force arrived, but alas! too late to save the town and the gallant soldier who had died in its defence. A new Khartoum has risen over the ruins left by the Mahdi's soldiers. Khartoum is a fine city, and one of its finest buildings is the Gordon Memorial College. But to all true Britons Gordon needs no memorial. His bravery and his patriotism will never die!

13

Clan Maclean

The Clan Maclean – or Clan Gillian, to give it the older name – consisted of four separate branches. No one of these branches was overlord of the others, because they all held their lands from the Lord of the Isles. There were Macleans of Duart, Maclaines of Lochbuie, Macleans of Coll, and Macleans of Ardgour. Of the four, the Macleans of Duart were the most influential. Their founder was called Lachlan; he became Steward of the Lord of the Isles, whose daughter he married.

The question, 'Then who is Chief of *all* the Macleans?' would be rather difficult to answer. Coll and Ardgour would probably not dispute the claims of Duart to that distinction, because they were, without doubt, branches of the Duart Clan. And although the Lochbuie family was also descended from Duart, their branch was from a Duart of a much earlier date and they refuse to acknowledge the claim of the Duart Chief to the chiefdom of *all* the Macleans!

It is a strange and rather sad thing that of all the great properties which once belonged to the two greater branches, only a few acres remain in their possession.

The origin of the Macleans is a matter of uncertainty. One opinion is that they are of Norman descent. But tradition gives it that the Clan was descended from a famous Celtic warrior who was known as 'Gillian-na-Tuaigh' ('Gillian of the Battle-axe'). And certainly the Macleans use as their crest a battle-axe between laurel and cypress branches. There is, of course, a story connected with the crest. It is that Gillian was engaged in a stag-hunt on Ben Talaidh, a mountain in Mull, and that in the excitement of the chase he wandered away from the rest of the party. A thick mist came down and enveloped the mountain and he completely lost his way. He wandered about for three days without being able to regain the lost track or find his companions. Then, being utterly tired out, he crept under a laurel bush and after fixing the handle of the battle-axe in the earth, he lay down and slept the sleep of exhaustion. When evening came, his friends who had been seeking him saw the head of the axe above the bush and, when they looked underneath, there was Gillian sleeping on the ground with his arm round the handle! It was said that at the Battle of Largs the same battle-axe did great execution among Haco's men.

The Macleans have royal Stewart blood in their veins, for a Maclean of Duart married a daughter of Alexander Stewart, Earl of Mar, who was grandson of Robert II. The grandson of this pair led Clan Maclean at Flodden and there he fell, it is said, in trying to save the life of James IV by placing his body between the King and the English arrows.

Another great family into which the Macleans married was that of the Earl of Argyll. The marriage of one of the Argylls (in the sixteenth century) was far from happy and, according to an old legend, her husband, Lachlan Maclean, made up his mind to get rid of his wife. No doubt there were faults on both sides. Rumour says that the lady had more than once tried to kill her husband! Still, it was a pretty cold-blooded scheme of his to have her placed on a rock which was exposed at low tide, and left there, with the horrible prospect of being surrounded and eventually drowned when the tide rose! The rock, which is still known as the 'Lady's Rock', lies between the coast of Mull and the Island of Lismore, and has always been a danger to shipping. Luckily for Lady Elizabeth a boat happened to come that way and she was rescued from her terrible plight and taken to her brother's house. Her relations were naturally furious at the husband's conduct and, some time afterwards, when the Laird of Duart was in Edinburgh, a brother-in-law, Sir John Campbell, went to his lodging and finding the Laird in bed stabbed him with a dirk. So the insult to the proud family of Argyll was avenged!

Although the Macleans were related to the Macdonalds the two Clans were continually at variance. After bickerings which lasted for fully a century, proceedings came to a head between them in a violent battle over some lands on Islay. On the eve of this battle Sir Lachlan consulted a famous witch with regard to the prospects of his Clan in the battle which was before them. She warned him that, if he wished for success, on no account should he land on Islay on a Thursday; and that he must not drink out of a spring there called 'Strange Neil's Well'. Luck was certainly against Lachlan for, a storm coming up on the Thursday, he was compelled to run for the nearest land, which, as it happened, was Islay! And being very thirsty after landing, he drank deeply from a spring, not knowing that it was the very well which he had been warned against! People were very superstitious in those days and they believed that the disaster which followed was entirely due to his disregard of the witch's warning. But that was not all. Before the battle, a dwarf from Jura who was known as 'Dubh Sith' (Black Elf) went to Sir Lachlan and offered to help him. Maclean disdained the assistance of such a little fellow and only laughed. The dwarf, full of rage at the contempt of the big man, went and offered himself to the leader on the other side, who promptly accepted his help. Of course no one expected 'Dubh Sith' to fight on equal terms with the brawny Highlanders, but he had his own way of doing things. He was a nimble climber and he made for a high tree from which he could see the fighters. He saw Sir Lachlan climb a little knoll from which to overlook the course of the battle, and his sharp eyes noted an open joint in Sir Lachlan's armour. He fitted an arrow to his bowstring, carefully took aim, and the arrow finding the open joint ended Maclean's life! Both sides had great numbers killed and wounded in this fight, which is known as the battle of the Rhinns of Islay.

The Maclaines of Lochbuie were nearly as famous as the Duart family. They had great possessions which included part of the mainland and the islands of Tiree, Jura, Scarba and Mull. When one of the chiefs of Lochbuie died, his heir was only a baby, called Murdoch Gearr. Maclean of Duart, seeing his chance, invaded and seized the lands of the infant heir. He would have seized the child as well, but some kindly people managed to convey him secretly to Ireland. There he was cared for, and when he grew up he determined to try and regain his own estates. With a number of brave Irishmen he set sail for Mull. On his arrival, he was recognised by his old nurse, who knew him by a mole on his breast. She persuaded her husband who was doorkeeper of the Castle of Lochbuie to open the gate, and the young heir rushed in at the head of his supporters. Having in this way taken the occupants of the castle by surprise, he soon made himself its master. The two branches of the Clan fought a pitched battle near Grulin in which the Duart Macleans were defeated. When Lochbuie was returning home in triumph after the battle, he came across Duart with a party of men asleep on the ground. Lcohbuie drew his dirk and cautiously twisted it in his rival's hair, sticking its point into the ground. When Maclean of Duart awoke and found his hair fastened to the ground, he recognised the dirk and the generosity of his rival in not killing him when he had the opportunity. He never afterwards interfered with Maclaine of Lochbuie and the two families were friends from that time onwards.

In Highland history there are a great many examples of the fidelity of clansmen to their Chief. One of them is found in the origin of the Maclean slogan – or war-cry – 'Another for Hector!' In the Battle of Inverkeithing between Cromwell's troops and those of Charles II, a father and seven sons are known to have sacrificed themselves for their Chief, Sir Hector Maclean of Duart. In the fight the Macleans were surrounded by the English and were being cut to pieces. Seeing that the aim of the enemy was to kill or capture the Chief, the old man and

his sons surrounded Sir Hector, and at every attempt on
his life one of them thrust himself forward to take the fatal
blow, crying, 'Another for Hector!' and the eight
Macleans lay dead before Sir Hector fell. There is an old
ballad about it which begins:

> Sir Hector Roy, the stout Maclean,
> Fought, one to ten, but all in vain,
> His broad claymore unsheathing:
> Himself lay dead 'mid heaps of slain
> For Charles at Inverkeithing.

When the Rebellion of 1715 broke out, the Chief, Sir
John Maclean, fought with his Clan on the Stewart
side. Then it was known that Prince Charlie was
coming, Sir Hector, the Chief in 1745, crossed over from
France to Edinburgh with the intention of assisting. As
part of his first equipment he wanted a good stout pair of
brogues for campaigning, and, knowing that one of his
clansmen in Edinburgh made good shoes, he went to him
to place an order, asking him to keep the purpose for
which they were intended a secret. But the shoemaker's
wife was so proud of having the Chief in her home that
she could not keep the secret! The authorities heard of it
and they promptly arrested Sir Hector and kept him safe
for two years! So he was not with the Clan at Culloden
where they fought in the first line.

In comparatively recent times a Maclean had the
unusual experience of being kidnapped by bandits
and held to ransom. This happened in 1907 to Sir
Harry Maclean (of Drimnin) whose Eastern title was
'Kaid Maclean'. He was instructor to the Moorish
army, afterwards becoming colonel of the Sultan of
Morocco's bodyguard. While on a mission from the
Sultan he was captured by Mulai ben Mohammed
Raisuli, a Moroccan bandit, who had terrorised the
whole district round Tangier with his outrages on
Europeans and natives alike. To take captive a well-
known Scotsman like Sir Harry Maclean was a piece
of cool audacity. But, once captured, Raisuli steadily
refused to let him go until the enormous sum of
£20 000 was paid as ransom. And at the end of eight
months the British Government had to pay it.

A recent Chief of the Macleans, Colonel Sir Fitzroy Donald Maclean was ninety six years of age. He served in the Crimean War, getting his commission from the great Duke of Wellington.[1]

Hundreds of years of Clan fighting naturally make a hardy race of soldiers and the Macleans have never been backward in military service. In 1775 a battalion commanded by Lieut.-Col. Alan Maclean of Torloisk was raised from Highlanders who had settled in Canada, and was used for active service there. In the Great War, Canada raised a battalion called the Maclean Highlanders. This battalion fought splendidly in France, and when the war was over they sent their banners to Duart Castle where they hang side by side with the colours of the old 84th Regiment in the hall of that ancient place, which is once more the natural centre of all descendants of the 'Children of the Mist' – Clan Gillean.

[1] His boyhood's ambition to restore the ruined walls of the ancestral home was realised when Duart Castle came into his possession in the year 1911, and the old home was re-established.

14

Clan Macleod

TRADITION reports that Leod, the earliest ancestor of the Macleods, was a royal viking – no less a personage than the son of Olaf, the Black King of Man! That is how the Macleods are entitled to use in their coat-of-arms the three legs which form the armorial bearings of the Isle of Man.

Leod married the heiress of Dunvegan who was the daughter of a Norwegian chief. They had two sons, Tormod, who founded the family of Macleod of Harris and Dunvegan; and Torquil, whose race held the Lewis and Assynt.

One of the most interesting of Tormod's descendants was Rory Mor of Dunvegan, who raised himself from the position of an outlawed chief to one of honour in the Highlands. When James VII was King of Scotland, he found confusion about the ownership of land in the Highlands and Islands, and he ordered all chiefs to produce the charters to their estates. Both families of Mcleod resisted the order: he therefore declared their land forfeit. A large number of people were brought from Fifeshire to settle on the Island of Lewis, but the Macleods saw to it that they had no peace in their new surroundings, and after a dangerous and uncomfortable time they went back to Fife. The experiment was tried three times without success, so in the end the King gave up the scheme. Rory Mor was able to get a free pardon and afterwards was given a knighthood by the King. Rory turned out a most successful ruler of his estates, doing his best to secure peace among his neighbours. He was the first of the family who could write. An earlier chief who had occasion to sign his name to a document had to have his hand guided like a child.

Dunvegan Castle, the family seat of Tormod's branch of the Macleods, built by Norsemen in the ninth or tenth century, is situated on precipitous rocks at the head of Loch Bracadale in the north-west of Skye. It is believed to be the oldest inhabited house in Scotland, and certainly is one of the most romantic. Many interesting relics are treasured in the Castle. There is an ancient cup or chalice of great beauty which Sir Walter Scott wrote about in *The Lord of the Isles*. Then there is the drinking-horn of Rory Mor, which is a great ox-horn, tipped with silver. It holds two pints of liquid and when a Macleod Chief comes of age, he is expected to be able to drain its contents at one draught! The crest and motto of the Macleods are a bull's head and the words 'Hold fast!' The story which they commemorate is one told of a Dunvegan chief who went to Inveraray to visit the Earl of Argyll. He arrived upon a fateful day, the day when, for some offence, one of the Campbell clansmen had been condemned by Argyll to be gored to death by a bull. A sort of arena had been prepared, from the raised seats of which Argyll and his guests could view the wretched man's death. At the hour arranged, the bull, bellowing with rage, was brought in and afterwards the man, who, whatever his feelings were, showed no fear as he faced the powerful animal. Macleod begged

Argyll to pardon him. 'Impossible,' said Argyll. 'Nothing can save him now!' 'But,' said Macleod, as he rose and threw off his cloak, 'if I save him will you give him to me?' 'Oh yes,' said Argyll, 'if you save him he is yours, but I warn you, you go to your death!' Quick as thought Macleod sprang into the arena, rushed to the bull, whose head was now lowered for the fatal thrust, and seized one of the horns with his left hand. As he did so the cry 'Hold fast!' rang out from one of the spectators. And 'hold fast' he did! The next moment he struck a blow with his dirk which pierced its heart and the great animal fell dead! There are still Campbells at Dunvegan who claim to be descended from the man whom Macleod saved.

Perhaps the most curious of the many relics at Dunvegan is the Brattich Shithe, or consecrated banner of the Clan, commonly called the Fairy Flag. It is like a pennon and is made of silk, with what look rather like berries of reddish colour, worked or sewed on the silk. There are two legends relating how it came into the possession of the Macleods. One tells that a fairy princess whom a Macleod married was called back to fairyland, and that as she fled she dropped her cloak. It is said that the Fairy Flag is the cloak the princess left behind! And the other story is that once upon a time an heir having been born to one of the chiefs, there were of course great rejoicings at Dunvegan. While the infant slept, his nurse stole away

to look on at the gay doings, and in her absence the bedclothes slipped off the babe. Then fairies, who were watching over him, wrapped him in the silken flag, and when the nurse returned and found the strange covering upon the child she carried the babe, wrapped as he was, into the great hall. As she entered there came the sound of fairy voices which told that the flag they had used had magic powers; that, if produced in battle, it would make an enemy see many time the number of Macleods who were actually there; that it would ensure the succession of the family; and that it would bring herring (which meant prosperity) into the Loch. But it must be used only three times, for, if waved on a fourth occasion, the flag and its bearer would disappear from earthly ken. It is said that it has been used twice with results exactly as promised by the fairies!

The Macleods, like the Macleans, were continually at variance with the Clan Macdonald. Three weeks after a very hot fight – in which the Macleods had the worst of it – Rory Mor Macleod was giving a feast to some of his clansmen in Harris. That night there was a great storm and after one tremendous gust of wind Rory exclaimed, 'What a night is this! If my greatest enemy were to ask shelter from me to-night, I would not refuse it!' He was very much taken aback when he was told that some of the Macdonalds (who were on their way to Skye) had been caught in the storm and had run for Harris; and that, even then, 'Donald Mac Ian 'Ic Sheumais' was at his door! Rory would not go back on his word, so the Macdonalds were invited to come in and sit down to supper. All was going well when one of them made an indiscreet remark about the recent fight. Instantly every Macleod sprang to his feet, weapon in hand, – but a shout from the Macleod Chief rang out above the storm, ordering his clansmen to sit down and not disgrace his hospitality! The Macdonalds were given sleeping-quarters in a house nearby, but before they left the castle a young servant gave them a significant hint that 'the wind was now fair for Skye!' Acting on it they quietly returned to their ship and set sail. Well for them that they did so, for one Macleod must have forgotten the honour of his Chief, and from the sea they saw great flames rising from the very house in which they were supposed to be sleeping!

In comparison with the Macleods of Dunvegan and Harris, the Macleods of Lewis and Assynt had a very chequered career. Their race began with a Torquil and ended with a Torquil. At the end of the sixteenth century their branch of the Clan was extinguished by the Mackenzies of Kintail who were also connections by marriage. The story of their extinction is one of the most painful chapters in Highland history, for it is one long record of murder and treachery. Mackenzie was aided and abetted by some Macleods who bore a grudge to Black Torquil, the last Chief – and one must allow that Torquil had in various ways earned the dislike of his neighbours. Whether or not, he was invited to bring his followers to a banquet on board a wine-carrying Dutch vessel which had been captured off Raasay. Scarcely had the guests seated themselves when they were all seized, tied with cords and carried off to Kintail in West Ross, where Mackenzie ordered that they should be beheaded. At the hour fixed for the execution there came a violent earthquake which terrified everybody – including the executioners. But it did not hinder them from committing the terrible deed; in fact it is said that they hurried to get it over! Mackenzie in this way came into possession of Lewis and Assynt. The chiefdom passed to the Macleods of Raasay, and, when their line failed, it went to Macleod of Cadboll in Easter Ross.

A Macleod chief at one time married the widow of a Mathieson, chief of Lochalsh. The union so much displeased her young sons that one of them went to his grandfather, the Mackintosh, and asked for assistance to turn Macleod out of the Castle of Lochalsh. He returned with a following and attacked the castle which Macleod and his wife defended. At last the attackers set fire to the building and then young Mathieson took up position at the gate, so as to allow his mother – but not his stepfather – to pass out. When she went he was relieved to know that she was safe, but you can imagine his anger when he found that, in the confusion, Macleod had passed out along with her, sheltered under her big plaid!

Two events occurred in those olden days which must bring regret to all Macleods. After the great Duke of Montrose was defeated at Carbisdale in Ross-shire, he wandered westwards, his only food for four days being a little bread and milk from a poor cottar's wife; and he gave himself up to Macleod of Assynt, from whom he had reason to expect assistance. Instead of getting help, he found himself a prisoner, and Macleod handed him over to the Covenanters. From Assynt he was taken to Edinburgh and executed. The darkest blot on the Macleods is the Eigg Massacre in 1577, when the whole population of the Island of Eigg was suffocated in a cave.

But it is unnecessary to dwell on these terrible times, now long past, when violence and bloodshed were rather the rule than the exception in the western Highlands and Islands. At the time of the Jacobite Rising of 1745 the Macleods were divided in their sympathies. The Macleods of Raasay were all for Prince Charlie, but the Chief took the other side. All the same, carefully kept among the treasures at Dunvegan are various relics of Prince Charlie and Flora Macdonald. Indeed, one of the Prince's most devoted companions during his wanderings in the islands after his defeat at Culloden was a Macleod.

From some information given by 'the Chevalier de Macleot' at Lisle in 1787, there would seem to have been a considerable branch of the Clan settled in France since 1530, descended from David MacLeod, Gendarme of the Scottish Guard. 'The present head of the family (1794) is Jean Nicolas de Macleot, Seigneur de Terreigne Pierreville, before the Revolution, gentilhomme ordinair du Roi.'

In modern times the most famous member of the Clan was the great divine, Dr Norman Macleod. He belonged to the Morven branch and had a distinguished career as a minister of the Church of Scotland and as a writer. He became a chaplain to Queen Victoria and for many years was her trusted friend. He is spoken of by Scottish people, all the world over, as 'the great Dr Norman Macleod'.

And just a word about the MacCrimmons, that most famous family of Scottish pipers. They are a sept of the Macleods, and for centuries they have been hereditary pipers to the chiefs of the Clan. Their piping was so wonderful that the Skye people said they owed their arts to fairy help! After the last Jacobite Rising an Act of Parliament abolished among other things the retaining of pipers by the chiefs, and the greatness of the MacCrimmons waned, as one by one they disappeared. The last of the MacCrimmons prepared to go to Canada and, before going, it is said he composed the famous lament called *Ha til, ha til, ha til, MacCrimmon!* ('No more, no more, no more, MacCrimmon!') He reached Greenock, but he never embarked, for the love of Skye drew him home again to his beloved island, and there he lived until his death in 1822 at ninety-one years of age.

15

Clan Ross – or Clan Anrias

THE origin of Ross as a Clan name is easy to understand. It is taken from the name of the County of Ross. But the alternative name, Clan Anrias, admits of more than one explanation. The best known is that a member of the Clan in olden days was a monk or abbot devoted to the service of St Andrew, the Patron Saint of Scotland; there is another which will be told in due course. It is contained in a curious sixteenth-century manuscript which was found among other old documents at Balnagown Castle, the family seat of the Rosses. It is called 'Ane breve Cronicle of the Erlls of Ross' and it begins by telling how the first earl got his title. The historian who deciphered the manuscript said that the dates in the story are by no means historically accurate. But seven hundred years separate from our own day the particular incident about which he was doubtful, so most people will be content to accept it as it stands! The story is related as follows. When Edward I became King of England there was a great concourse of people from all parts of the country to see the Coronation festivities in London, and representatives of all the great Scottish families were invited to attend, because Margaret, the Scottish

Queen, was the sister of the new King. At that time there was at the English Court a famous French wrestler from Normandy. This wrestler was marvellously strong and so skilful in the art that, although he had been challenged over and over again, no one had been able to overthrow him. But during the gay doings at the Coronation he was challenged by Farquhar Ross, a vassal of King Alexander, from the far north of Scotland, and to the amazement of the Court and the delight of the Scottish King, Farquhar overthrew and finally vanquished the great fighter! King Alexander was so pleased with Farquhar's 'notabill vassalage' – as he called it – that he gave him the Earldom of Ross. Farquhar gave the credit of his victory to a vow that he had made that, if he should be victorious in the fight, he would found an abbey of the first religious Order whose members he should happen to meet in Scotland. On his way to the north he came across two 'white canons' (or monks) from Whithorn Abbey in Galloway, and he took them home with him to Ross-shire. He founded an abbey of this Order at Fearn near Kincardine in Ross, which later fell into disrepair, so another abbey was built at Fearn in Easter Ross, which is in use to-day as a Parish Church.

From Farquhar five Earls of Ross descended, all of whom made marriages of importance. One of them married the sister of Robert the Bruce – who was a personal friend and for whom he fought at Bannockburn. And the daughter of Earl Hugh became the second wife of Robert II of Scotland. At that time Scotland and England were at war and Earl Hugh was killed in the defeat of the Scots at Halidon Hill near Berwick, where the English forces carried all before them. After that, the storm centre of all the fighting between the two nations was the City of Perth, which is the gate of the Highlands, as well as an important vantage point of mid Scotland. The people of Perth must have had a most uncomfortable time in those days for the city was held sometimes by the Scots and sometimes by the English. During the last time that the English held the city they spent vast sums fortifying it, so that to the Scots besiegers it seemed impregnable. Even when French ships of war sailed up the River Tay, the moat which surrounded the town prevented the placing of the Scots engines of war within firing distance. The Earl of Ross hit at length upon the solution of the difficulty. He brought a large body of miners upon the scene and directed them to excavate underground; in this way all the water from the moat was drained away. The engines of war could then be brought up and placed against the walls of the city. Even the heavens helped the Scots, for on the day fixed for the attack there was an eclipse of the sun which terrified the garrison. And although the besieging army also felt far from comfortable about such an unusual phenomenon, they realised the advantage which the growing darkness gave them and took the chance to place their pieces in readiness. When the eclipse passed, the English Governor saw the strong position of the Scots and he came to terms and gave up the town.

Earl William, the hero of Perth, had two daughters, but no heir. The younger daughter married Donald, Lord of the Isles, and Euphemia was heiress to her father. She was courted by Walter Lesley from Aberdeenshire who is called in the 'Breve Cronicle' a 'nobill valzeant man'. She liked the noble valiant Lesley very much, but she liked the name of Ross still better, and she refused to marry him unless he would take *her* name. He agreed and became Walter Ross, and their son was Alexander, Earl of Ross. The line of the ancient earls ended with Alexander's daughter, who became a nun and resigned her claim to the earldom in favour of her uncle, the Earl of Buchan.

Then Donald, Lord of the Isles, claimed the earldom for his wife, who was also a Ross. Donald gathered a great army and marched into Ross-shire, sweeping all before him. His success so emboldened him that he took his army right across Scotland, carrying destruction in his path. In Aberdeenshire the Earl of Mar had assembled an army to meet the marauders and a great battle took place at Harlaw near Inverurie. All day long the battle raged, with dreadful slaughter on both sides, and with the advantage to the Lord of the Isles. Darkness fell, and Mar and the survivors had to pass the night on the field of battle in full expectation that with morning light there would be renewed attack. When day dawned it was found that the Lord of the Isles had retreated and was well on his way westwards! And although there were new hostilities later he was compelled to resign his claim to the Earldom of Ross and become instead a vassal to the Scottish Crown. This battle left its result on the music and folk history of the country. For many years a march called *The Battle of Harlaw* was very popular throughout Scotland; and so was a ballad which describes the meeting of the armies and the progress of the battle – and what happened after:

> 'Then Donald fled and that full fast,
> To mountains hich for all his micht,
> For he and his were all agast,
> And ran till they were out of sicht.
> And sua [so] of Ross he lost his richt,
> Thoch mony men with him he brocht
> Towards the Yles fled day and nicht,
> And all he wan was deirlie bocht.'

The Lairds of Balnagown were descended from Hugh, Earl of Ross, who was killed at Halidon Hill. (His second son, Hugh, was Laird of Balnagown and Rarichie). The fifth Laird in this line married Katharine McLendris, daughter of Paul MacTyre McLendris, and in the 'Breve Cronicle' we read 'after whilk marriage *Ross are called Clan Lendris*': so that is the second explanation of the name 'Clan Anrias'.

There is a funny old legend at the end of the 'Breve Cronicle' of the 'Erlls of Ross' which links the origin of Paul MacTyre with that of the Macleods. According to the legend: There were three sons of the King of Denmark who came over the sea and landed in the northern parts of Scotland to conquer by the sword and gain lands for themselves. Ewine conquered Caithness; Loid (or Leod) conquered the lands of the Lewis, and Lendris conquered a part of Sutherland and that part of Ross which belonged to the Earls of Ross. Paul MacTyre was the grandson of that Lendris. He was powerful and ruthless, and in his day was a sort of Northern Rob Roy. The manuscript calls him 'ane takand man' – which is another way of saying that he helped himself! Cattle were the form of blackmail which he mainly extorted from weaker people, and it was reported that every year, as long as he was fit to travel, he took nine score of cattle out of Caithness alone! When he became infirm his son went in his stead to take toll of the Caithness cattle. But while the Caithness folks were in dread of Paul and never dared to resist him, they had no feeling of that sort for Murthro Reoch, his son, for they banded themselves together and lay in wait for him and killed him. When the news reached the father the manuscript tells that he 'deyit for displeasor of his sone'. Later the friends of the family sent for the bones of the dead Murthro that they might be laid in his father's grave, and there is a queer old rhyme which tells what happened:

'This Murthro Reoch of whome ye now do
    reid
Throw tyrannie was slaine as ye heir tell.
The eldest sone of Paul MacTyre indeed
Was buryed in Caithness quhair the caise
    befell.
Quhen freindis tharafter taik yame to counsell
And send in haist ane young man for his
    baines
Quha coming home with them in Helmisdaill
Drownit thairin he and they all at aines.'

The messenger apparently tried to cross the Moray Firth from Helmsdale and met with disaster. Seafaring people consider that a dead body in a boat always brings ill-luck, and no doubt the misfortune was looked upon as a judgment.

The Balnagown line of Rosses failed when David, the thirteenth Laird, had no heir, and the estate was conveyed to the Rosses of Hawkhead, an old family of great repute, but in no way related to the family of the ancient earls. And, rather curiously, in the fifteenth century a member of this Ross family was chosen to be one of the Scottish champions to fight with three knights of Burgundy in the presence of James II; and for the second time in their history a Ross defeated a Frenchman in a king's Court!

The Rosses have made their mark in many spheres of life. Just a hundred years ago, a contribution to the knowledge of the polar regions, which sent a wave of interest through the scientific world, was made by Rear-Admiral Sir John Ross and his nephew, Rear-Admiral Sir James Clark Ross. They discovered the magnetic North Pole, and after planting the British flag there they returned home with a collection of valuable scientific data. This stood Sir James Clark Ross in good stead when he was appointed to command an expedition to the Antarctic, during which he discovered a mountainous land which he named Victoria Land, and a smoking volcano, which he named after his ship, Mount Erebus. In memory of this explorer, the sea which bounds that rocky coastline was called the Ross Sea. And so, in that far southern land, there will live for ever a name which brings to Scottish minds not only the brave man for whose sake it was given, but also thoughts of that beautiful romantic county in the far north of Scotland which is the cradle of the great Ross Clan.

16

Clan Graham

IT is about nineteen hundred years since the Romans came to Britain and took possession of all the flat part of England and part of the south of Scotland.

They planned to conquer the Highlands also but the Highlanders offered determined opposition to that. They considered that a supply of food for their soldiers would be very hard to get in such rocky country, so they contented themselves and built a long wall from the Firth of Forth to the Firth of Clyde. They made watch-towers along the wall and established camps, at intervals, to make certain that if they could not get into the Highlands, neither should the inhabitants get out! This did not please the Highlanders at all. The country from which the wall excluded them was fine rich land, just as useful to them as it was to the Romans. Some day, they determined, all that would be changed.

At last, early in the fifth century, the clansmen assembled in great numbers, made a determined attack upon the wall and managed to breach it. And the first man to get over the wall was a Graham!

There is a rival explanation. It is that the name Grahame or Grime is taken from the Norse word

'Grimr' – meaning Devil – and that the wall was called Grime's or Devil's Dyke because people thought it was too wonderful to have been made by the hands of men.

Whatever truth there is in the story, the remaining part of the wall is still called Graham's Dyke, and appears under this name in the old maps.

There are very few families, Sir Walter Scott says, which can boast of historical renown such as that of the Grahams.

The name occurred in records in the twelfth century, when William of Graham was granted the lands of Abercorn and Dalkeith. In the following century land near Montrose was granted to his grandson by William the Lion.

One member of the Clan in the following generation married the daughter of the Earl of Strathearn and acquired lands in Perthshire where later many branches of the Clan settled. A son of this marriage, Sir John the Graham of Dundaff, was the bosom friend of Wallace. He fell at Falkirk, fighting for Scotland's freedom. His epitaph in Latin, translated, runs as follows:

'Here lys
Sir John the Graeme, baith wight and wise,
Ane of the Chiefs reskewit Scotland thrice;
Ane better knight not to the world was lent
Nor was gude Graham of truth and hardiment –'

and that is a pretty good description of many a Graham warrior since the time of Sir John the Graeme!

The family exchanged with Robert the Bruce the property of Cardross in Dumbartonshire, for Old Montrose in Forfarshire, from which they afterwards took their titles of nobility.

The marriage of a Graham clansman with the daughter of Robert III brought royal blood into the family, and the great-great-grandson of this pair became Earl of Montrose in recognition of his prowess at the Battle of Sauchieburn.

Four generations more and we come to James Graham, the fifth Earl, whose name has been handed down to posterity as 'The Great Montrose'.

He was one of the most prominent of the nobles who helped Scots people to resist the compulsion of Charles I in making their form of worship that of the Episcopal Church; and he assisted at the signing of the Covenant which was drawn up to defend their faith and preserve their religious freedom.

When an army was raised to support the Covenanters' cause Montrose conducted its successful campaign in Aberdeenshire and defeated Viscount Aboyne at Bridge of Dee.

Afterwards, for some reason, he became a convert to the Royalist side. He was created a marquis, and became lieutenant-general of the King's Forces in Scotland.

The leader in many a skirmish, he won several pitched battles for the Crown, and being a man of extraordinary resource and courage, he could inspire his army to great deeds.

At the Battle of Kilsyth, for instance, his men found themselves opposed for the first time by a regiment of cuirassiers, the sight of whose glittering armour seemed to strike terror to the hearts of Montrose's soldiers.

Montrose heard mutterings that it would be useless to try and fight men clad in iron, and he saw that the situation must be dealt with, or disaster would surely overtake him.

So he set himself to turn this ugly feeling of doubt into one of contempt; so riding up to the head of his cavalry and pointing to the cuirassiers, he addressed his men:

'Gentlemen, these are the men you beat at Alford the men who ran away from you at Auldearn and Tippermuir. They are such cowards that their officers could not induce them to face you unless they were protected by armour! To show our contempt we'll fight them *in our shirts*!' And with that he threw off his coat and waistcoat before them all. The effect was instantaneous.

His example was followed with the utmost enthusiasm by the whole army.

The day being very sultry, the physical relief from heavy uniforms helped the general feeling of uplift-ment. Montrose knew that, although there was stiff work to be got through first, the spirit of the men would help towards victory – and his faith was justified.

His next orders were that he should take his army to the Borders and get on the track of General Leslie's army – but now trouble began to brew. The Highlanders did not want to spend another winter away from their homes, and they withdrew – only for a time, they said.

The Earl of Aboyne and his countrymen were the next to forsake him, and he was left with a sadly reduced army. Then, before he could make up the numbers, he had to face the Battle of Philiphaugh, which was a complete disaster – and he had to flee to Norway.

Five years later, at the command of Charles II, he landed in Caithness with a small army and marched into Sutherland. And there at Carbisdale on the Kyle of Sutherland the military career of the Great Montrose ended.

After being a fugitive for four days he was captured by Macleod of Assynt and handed over to the Covenanters; and as a writer has described it – 'a life of meteoric splendour' closed on the gallows in the Grassmarket of Edinburgh. The great-grandson of the famous Earl – a very distinguished descendant – was the first Duke of Montrose.

A branch of the Clan which was closely identified with the Great Montrose was that of his cousin, Graham of Inchbrakie. When Montrose came in disguise from England to arrange about the Royalist rising, Inchbrakie received him at his House of Tullibelton, where in the park was a great yew tree whose foliage sheltered him from prying eyes on more than one occasion. When he raised the Stewart Standard at Blair Atholl, Inchbrakie was with him and was one of his chief officers during the campaign; but the Commonwealth soldiers when they came to Scotland made him suffer for his Royalism, for they burned down his castle and threw him into prison.

This Graham was the Laird to whose family a witch, named Kate McNiven, guaranteed perpetual possession of the estate of Inchbrakie. Kate was nurse to the Laird's little son and, although she was young, she was already learned in the black art of witchcraft.

She had an idea that the boy would bring her bad luck or even death, and she brooded over that idea until at last she tried to poison him. The boy disliked her as much as she disliked him, and she was eventually relieved of her duties.

Although she was branded as a sorceress it did not affect the kindliness of her old master towards her. But she played tricks on him all the same.

In those days when people went to any public function they took their own knives and forks with them!

One day Inchbrakie went to a festival at Dunning, and as usual he carried his knife and fork in his pocket and put them on the dinner-table.

He was much bothered by a bumble-bee which buzzed round his head at dinner and would not give him peace to eat. So he got up at last and chased it out of the window.

When he went back to his place at the table his knife and fork were nowhere to be seen, and, search as he liked – over the table and under the table – he could find no trace of them. It was a humiliating position! But when he got home his knife and fork were found in their usual place!

Of course people believed that Kate had turned herself into a bee in order to play this annoying trick!

Her evil deeds became notorious and at last evidences of her sorcery were collected and she was tried for witchcraft and condemned to be burnt.

Her old master did his best to help her, but the whole parish was against her release; so the stake was pitched and the faggots piled on the summit of the Knock of Crieff, and Kate was dragged to the stake in the presence of a huge crowd. When she was chained to the post, her eye lighted on Inchbrakie among the crowd, and, knowing that he had been her friend she asked that she might speak with him.

As he approached, she bent her head and bit off a large blue bead from a necklace which she was wearing. Spitting it out towards him she told him to keep it as a talisman, and so long as the bead was treasured, the family of Inchbrakie should never want a lineal heir, nor lose the ancestral property.

The bead, set in a ring, was kept as an heirloom in the family. It was said to be an uncut sapphire.

A Graham warrior, celebrated both in history and song, was John Graham of Claverhouse. He was born in 1649, and was of the same family as Montrose.

A staunch Jacobite, the Covenanters looked upon him as their deadly enemy. Such was their awe of him that they declared that he was not only proof against bullets, but that the black horse on which he always rode had been given him by the Devil!

On this horse Claverhouse was said to perform the most marvellous feats, flying like a bird along the sides of precipitous hills and treading safely through pathless bogs where an ordinary horse must have come to grief.

In 1688 he was second in command of the Scottish army and was ordered south to protect the Stewart throne, and oppose the landing of William of Orange.

At that time he was created Viscount Dundee, – the 'Bonnie Dundee' of the old song.

James II had fled to France, and Claverhouse coming back to Scotland, all his energy was bent on helping forward the Stewart cause.

He organised a great rising in the Highlands, where 'Bonnie Dundee' was a name with a charm.

The Jacobites flocked to his standard, and, in a great battle at Killiecrankie in 1689, King William's forces under Mackay were completely routed.

But rejoicing was turned into mourning, for, at the moment of victory a bullet ended the life of the brave leader and lost to Scotland one of her most gallant soldiers.

'So, amidst the battle's thunder,
Shot, and steel, and scorching flame,
In the glory of his manhood
Passed the spirit of the Graeme!

Sleep! – and till the latest trumpet
Wakes the dead from earth and sea;
Scotland shall not boast a braver
Chieftain than our own Dundee!'

AYTOUN.

The Border Grahames are descended from a famous swordsman, the second son of Malise, Earl of Strathearn, who was called 'Sir John with the Bright Sword'.

To a great tilting match given near Berwick by Henry of Lancaster (afterwards Henry IV of England), twenty Scots knights, renowned as swordsmen, were invited to come and tilt with twenty English lords, and prove their skill.

One of the Border Grahames tilted with the English Baron Talbot, whose life was saved only by the breast-plates he wore.

At supper an English knight challenged Grahame to tilt with him next day.

'Dost thou ask to tilt with me?' said Grahame. 'Rise early in the morning, confess your sins, and make your peace with God, for you shall sup in Paradise!'

Next morning Graham's sword ran the Englishman through the body and he died where he fell.

The Menteith Grahams were descended from Robert II through David, Earl of Strathearn.

One of them, being vain of his descent, boasted that 'he was as good as Charles I', and when the King was told he deprived him of the earldom.

A later member of the family was given the Earldom of Menteith and Airth.

The story is told that one of these Earls held a boasting match with Finlayson, the Town Clerk of Stirling.

The Earl asked the Clerk whether he had seen the sailing cherry-tree? 'No,' said Finlayson, 'What is that, my Lord?' The Earl said that a goose on the Lake of Menteith had once swallowed a cherry stone, and in due time a tree grew out of her mouth and could be seen when she was swimming round the lake. At present, he said, the tree was laden with cherries of the most wonderful flavour!

He challenged his guest to tell as wonderful a story. Finlayson was not easily beaten, so he said: 'Did your Lordship ever hear of the ball which was fired from one of Cromwell's cannon when he was at Airth?' 'No,' said the Earl. 'What is the tale?'

'It is this,' said the Clerk. 'The ball fired from Airth reached Stirling Castle and lodged in the mouth of a trumpet which one of the soldiers was sounding!'

'And I suppose the trumpeter was killed?' said Lord Menteith.

'Not at all!' said Finlayson. 'He blew the ball back again and killed the artilleryman who had fired it!'

After the Battle of Pinkie some Appin Stewarts on their way home called at the inn of Port of Menteith, tired, dejected and hungry.

In the inn they found a fine dinner of roasted hens which had been prepared for a marriage party of the Grahams at which the Earl of Menteith was to be a guest. The hungry Stewarts looked upon this as a veritable godsend, ate up everything and went on their way.

When the wedding party arrived and found what had happened they were naturally very wroth.

The Earl with a number of retainers pursued and fought the Stewarts, who added insult to injury by accompanying each sword-thrust with sneering references to the roasted hens. Most of the Stewarts were killed; but the origin of the quarrel earned for the Grahams the nickname of 'Gramoch-an-Garrigh', which is 'Graham of the Hens'.

Sometime afterwards, it is said, a Graham and a MacGregor quarrelled on the Hill of Coldon beside the Lake of Menteith.

MacGregor in the height of his passion was in the act of opening his mouth to call out 'Hen Grahams!' when, anticipating his intention, Graham drew his sword and severed the MacGregor's head from his body.

But his antagonist had the last word, for the head of the MacGregor rolled to the foot of the hill crying out 'Hen Grahams; Hen Grahams!' all the way to the bottom!